HMH

Virginia
Standards of Learning Success

POWERED BY
GO Math!

INCLUDES

- Virginia Standards of Learning Lessons
- Lesson Practice/Homework with Spiral Review

Table of Contents

Name _____

Number Sequences

Essential Question How can you write numbers in order?

Learning Objective You will learn to count and write numbers to 20 in and out of order.

Listen and Draw Real World

Count the dots. Write the numbers.

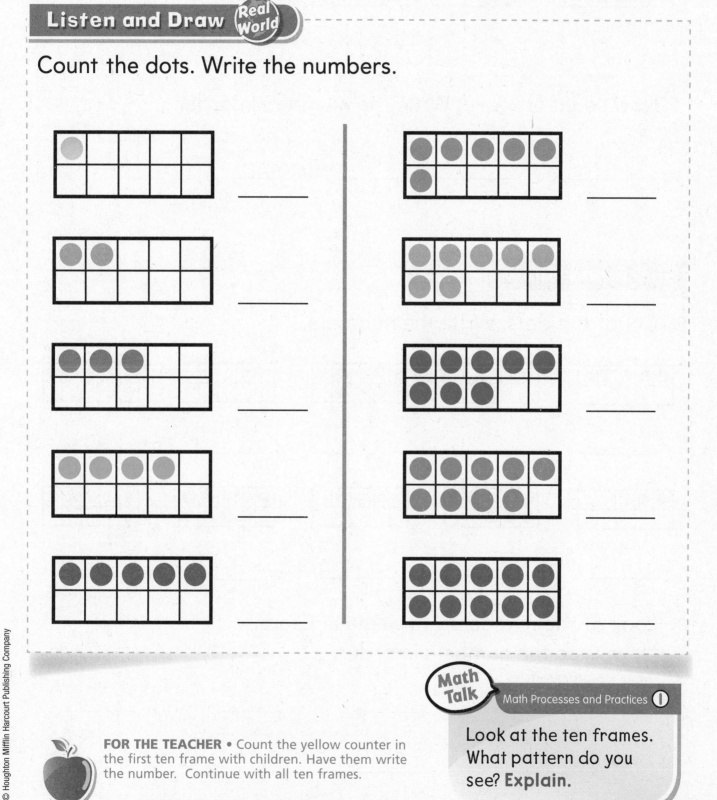

Math Talk

Math Processes and Practices ①

FOR THE TEACHER • Count the yellow counter in the first ten frame with children. Have them write the number. Continue with all ten frames.

Look at the ten frames. What pattern do you see? **Explain.**

Count the dots. Write the numbers.

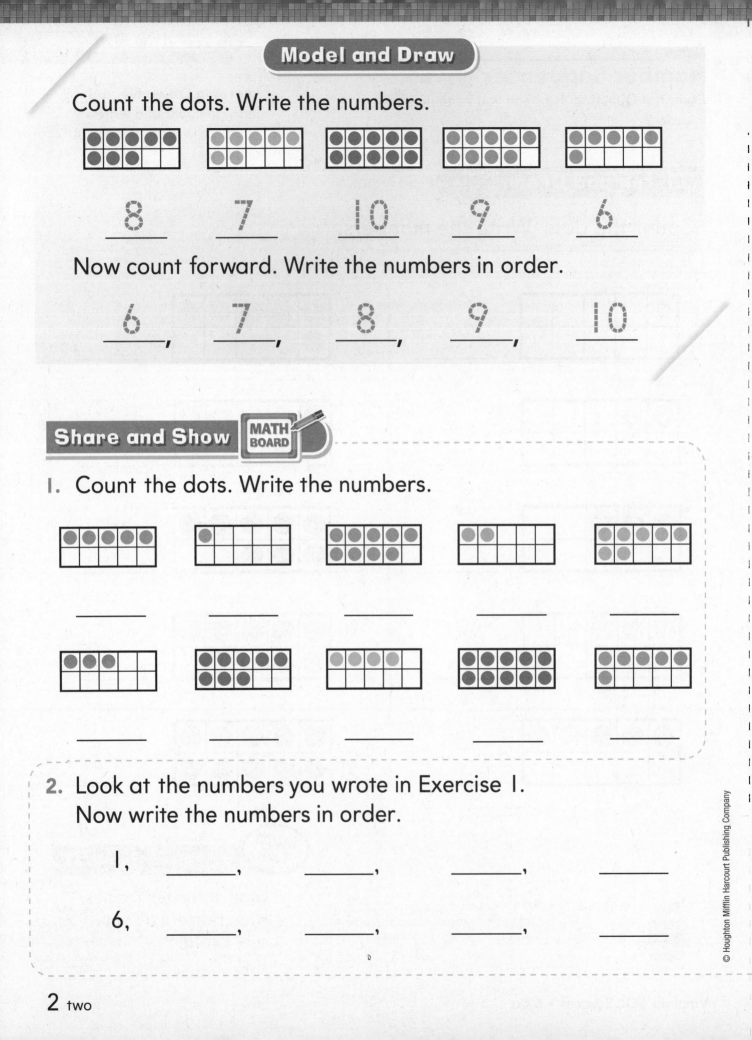

_8_   _7_   _10_   _9_   _6_

Now count forward. Write the numbers in order.

_6_ , _7_ , _8_ , _9_ , _10_

Share and Show MATH BOARD

1. Count the dots. Write the numbers.

_____   _____   _____   _____   _____

_____   _____   _____   _____   _____

2. Look at the numbers you wrote in Exercise 1.
   Now write the numbers in order.

   1, _____ , _____ , _____ , _____

   6, _____ , _____ , _____ , _____

On Your Own

Count the dots. Write the numbers.

3.

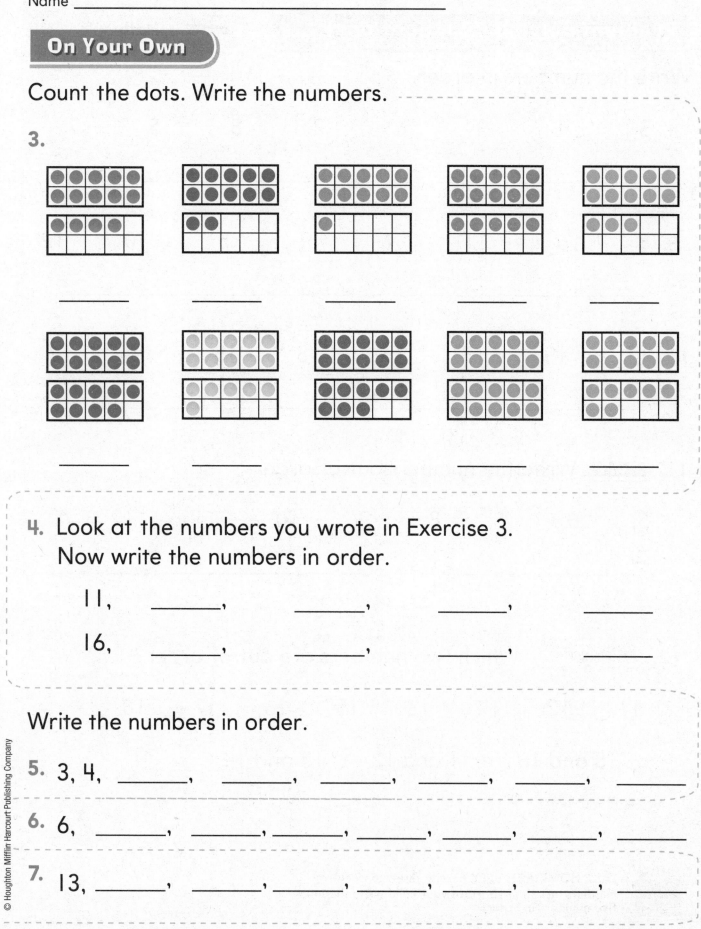

_____   _____   _____   _____   _____

_____   _____   _____   _____   _____

4. Look at the numbers you wrote in Exercise 3.
   Now write the numbers in order.

   11, _____,   _____,   _____,   _____

   16, _____,   _____,   _____,   _____

Write the numbers in order.

5. 3, 4, _____, _____, _____, _____, _____, _____

6. 6, _____, _____, _____, _____, _____, _____, _____

7. 13, _____, _____, _____, _____, _____, _____, _____

Problem Solving • Applications (Real World)   WRITE Math

Write the numbers in order.

8. 3   4   9   6   2   8   5   7

_____

9. 8   6   11   7   9   5   10   12

_____

10. 17   19   13   16   18   15   14   18

_____

11. GO DEEPER Write the numbers out of order.

5   6   7   8   9   10   11   12

_____

12. THINK SMARTER Which two numbers are out of order?

11   12   14   13   15   16   17   18

15 and 16   11 and 12   13 and 14

○   ○   ○

TAKE HOME ACTIVITY • Write three consecutive numbers less than 15. Have your child write the next five numbers in order.

Number Sequences

Learning Objective You will learn to count and write numbers to 20 in and out of order.

Count the dots in each set of ten frames. Write the numbers.

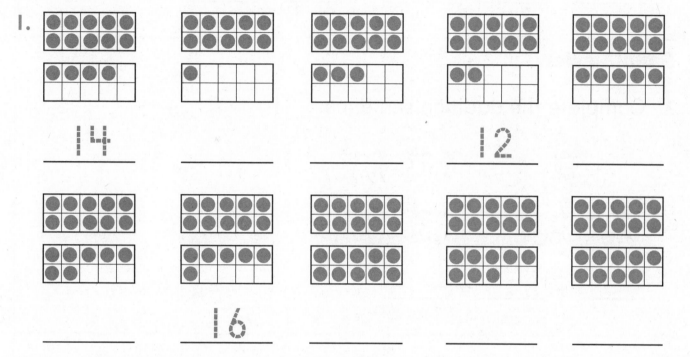

1. 14 ___ ___ 12 ___

16 ___ ___ ___ ___

Now write the numbers in order.

2. 11 , ___ , ___ , ___ , ___ ,

16 , ___ , ___ , ___ , ___ ,

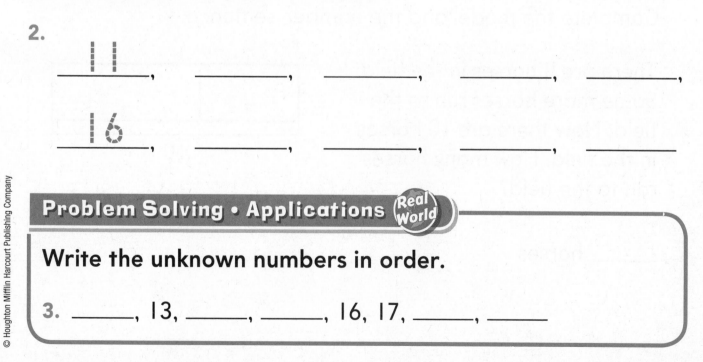

Problem Solving • Applications Real World

Write the unknown numbers in order.

3. _____, 13, _____, _____, 16, 17, _____, _____

Lesson Check

1. Write the numbers in order.

   <u>13</u>, <u>14</u>, <u>   </u>, <u>16</u>, <u>17</u>

Spiral Review

2. Complete the addition sentence.

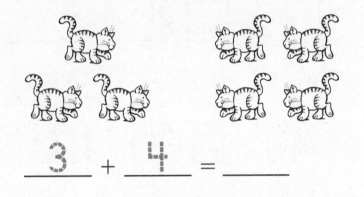

   <u>3</u> + <u>4</u> = <u>   </u>

---

3. Read the problem. Use the bar model to solve.
   Complete the model and the number sentence.

   There are 4 horses in the field.
   Some more horses run to the
   field. Now there are 10 horses
   in the field. How many horses
   ran to the field?

   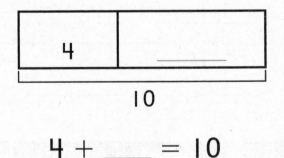

   $4 +$ ___ $= 10$

   _____ horses

Name _____

Ordinal Numbers

Essential Question How can you use ordinal numbers to identify position?

Learning Objective You will identify position using ordinal numbers.

 **Listen and Draw** (Real World)

You can use words to tell the position of each car in the line.

(Math Talk) Math Processes and Practices ①

How did you know which car to color red? **Explain.**

 FOR THE TEACHER • Read the following problem. There are five cars in a race. Count from the beginning of the line to the number 3. Color that car green. Use red to color the car in front of the green car. Use blue to color the car behind the green car.

Model and Draw

An **ordinal number** tells about position.

Circle the 2nd sailboat.
Mark an X on the 7th sailboat.

> Look at the direction of the sailboats. The sailboat at the end is 1st.

10th tenth	9th ninth	8th eighth	7th seventh	6th sixth	5th fifth	4th fourth	3rd third	2nd second	1st first

Share and Show · MATH BOARD

Use the picture below to answer the questions.

1st

1. Circle the 5th T-shirt.

2. Circle the 9th T-shirt.

3. In what position is the 👕?

_____

8 eight

On Your Own

Circle to show position.

4. Which bear is 6th?

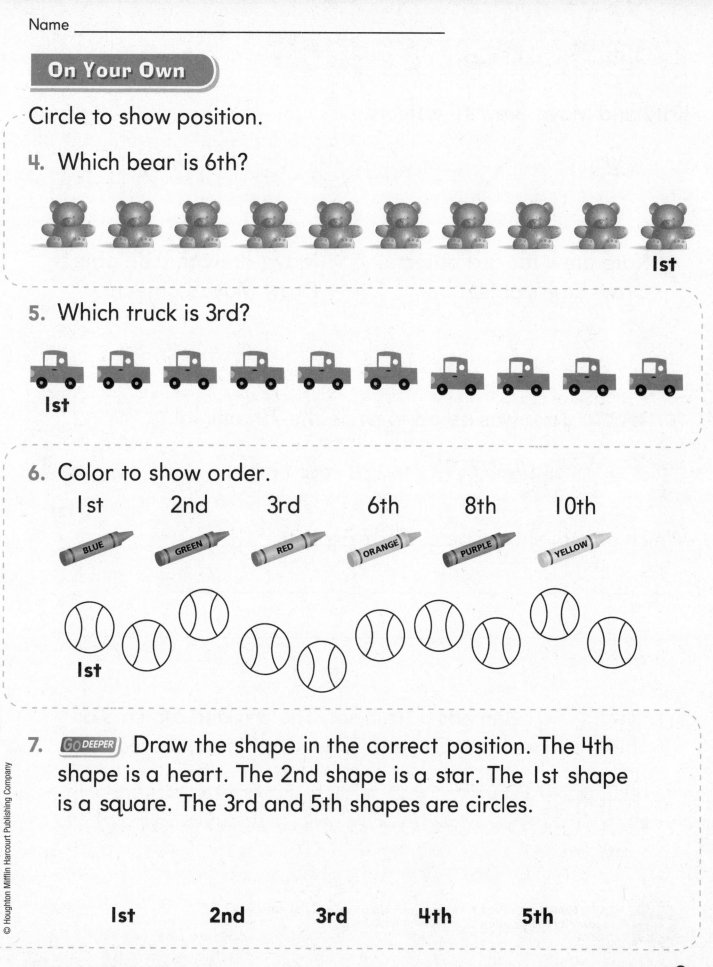

1st

5. Which truck is 3rd?

1st

6. Color to show order.

1st	2nd	3rd	6th	8th	10th
BLUE	GREEN	RED	ORANGE	PURPLE	YELLOW

1st

7. GO DEEPER Draw the shape in the correct position. The 4th shape is a heart. The 2nd shape is a star. The 1st shape is a square. The 3rd and 5th shapes are circles.

1st   2nd   3rd   4th   5th

Problem Solving • Applications (Real World)

Kate and Maya drew 10 objects.

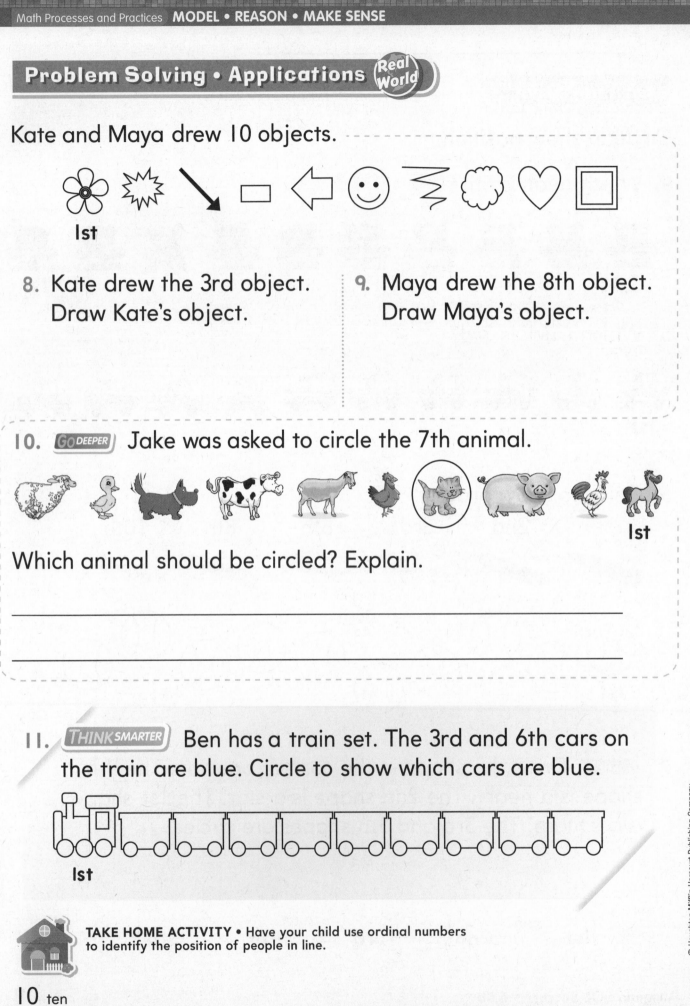

1st

8. Kate drew the 3rd object.
Draw Kate's object.

9. Maya drew the 8th object.
Draw Maya's object.

10. GO DEEPER Jake was asked to circle the 7th animal.

1st

Which animal should be circled? Explain.

_____

_____

11. THINK SMARTER Ben has a train set. The 3rd and 6th cars on the train are blue. Circle to show which cars are blue.

1st

TAKE HOME ACTIVITY • Have your child use ordinal numbers to identify the position of people in line.

10 ten

Name _____

Ordinal Numbers

Use the picture below to answer the questions.

Learning Objective You will identify position using ordinal numbers.

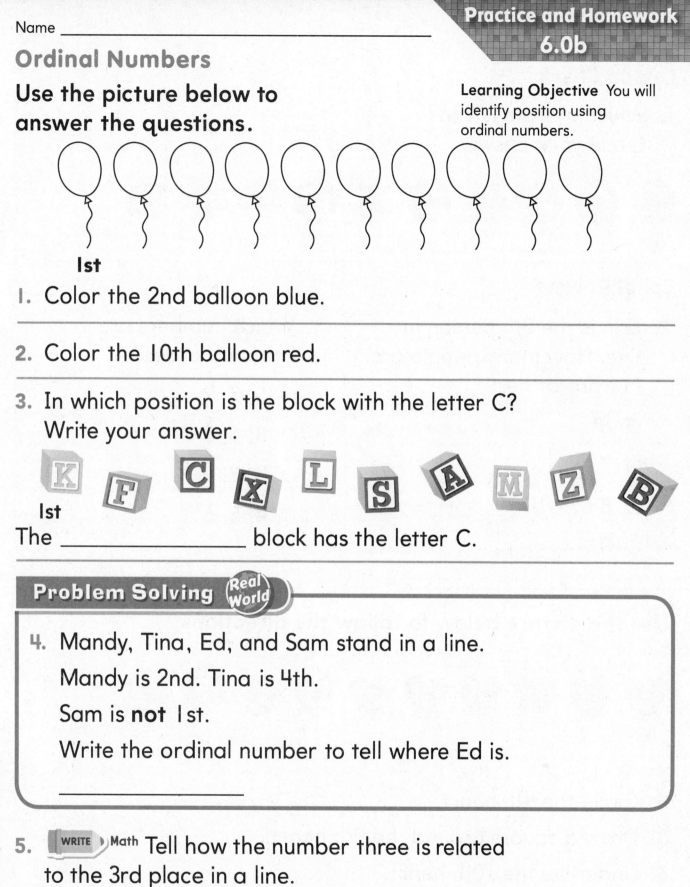

Ist

1. Color the 2nd balloon blue.

_____

2. Color the 10th balloon red.

_____

3. In which position is the block with the letter C? Write your answer.

K F C X L S A M Z B

Ist

The _____ block has the letter C.

_____

Problem Solving Real World

4. Mandy, Tina, Ed, and Sam stand in a line.

   Mandy is 2nd. Tina is 4th.

   Sam is **not** Ist.

   Write the ordinal number to tell where Ed is.

   _____

5. **WRITE** Math Tell how the number three is related to the 3rd place in a line.

_____

_____

Lesson Check

1. Which marble is 2nd?
   Circle your answer.

1st

Spiral Review

2. Erin is the 8th person in
   line. How many people are
   in front of her?

   ○ 6

   ○ 7

   ○ 8

   ○ 9

3. Which numbers are in
   counting order?

   ○ 5, 7, 4

   ○ 8, 6, 5

   ○ 4, 2, 9

   ○ 4, 5, 6

Use the picture below to follow the directions.

1st

4. Circle the 4th heart.

5. Draw a square around the 9th heart.

6. Underline the 10th heart.

Name _____

Count Forward and Backward by Ones

Essential Question How can knowing the counting pattern help you count forward and backward by ones?

Learning Objective You will learn to count forward and backward by ones.

Listen and Draw

Count forward. Write the numbers.

1 , ____ , ____ , ____ , ____ , ____ ____ , ____ , ____ , ____

Count backward. Write the numbers.

10 , ____ , ____ , ____ , ____ , ____ , ____ , ____ , ____ , ____

HOME CONNECTION • Your child has been working with number patterns. He or she identified the number pattern used and completed the missing numbers.

Math Talk How are counting forward and counting backward patterns different?. **Explain.**

Count forward from 13.

When you count forward, each number is one more.

13, __14__, __15__, __16__, __17__

Count backward from 13.

When you count backward, each number is one less.

13, __12__, __11__, __10__, __9__

Share and Show MATH BOARD

Count forward. Write the numbers.

1. 8, ___, ___, ___, ___

2. 23, ___, ___, ___, ___

3. 17, ___, ___, ___, ___

4. 11, ___, ___, ___, ___

5. 30, ___, ___, ___, ___

☑6. 26, ___, ___, ___, ___

Count backward. Write the numbers.

7. 22, ___, ___, ___, ___

8. 10, ___, ___, ___, ___

9. 16, ___, ___, ___, ___

10. 25, ___, ___, ___, ___

11. 30, ___, ___, ___, ___

☑12. 21, ___, ___, ___, ___

On Your Own

Count forward or backward. Write the numbers.

13. 11, 10, ____, ____, ____, ____, ____, ____, ____, ____

14. 2, 3, ____, ____, ____, ____, ____, ____, ____, ____

15. 30, 29, ____, ____, ____, ____, ____, ____, ____, ____

16. 18, 17, ____, ____, ____, ____, ____, ____, ____, ____

17. 17, 18, ____, ____, ____, ____, ____, ____, ____, ____

18. 21, 22, ____, ____, ____, ____, ____, ____, ____, ____

19. 9, 10, ____, ____, ____, ____, ____, ____, ____, ____

20. 25, 24, ____, ____, ____, ____, ____, ____, ____, ____

21. **Go DEEPER** Count forward or backward. Write the unknown numbers on the boats.

Problem Solving • Applications (Real World) WRITE Math

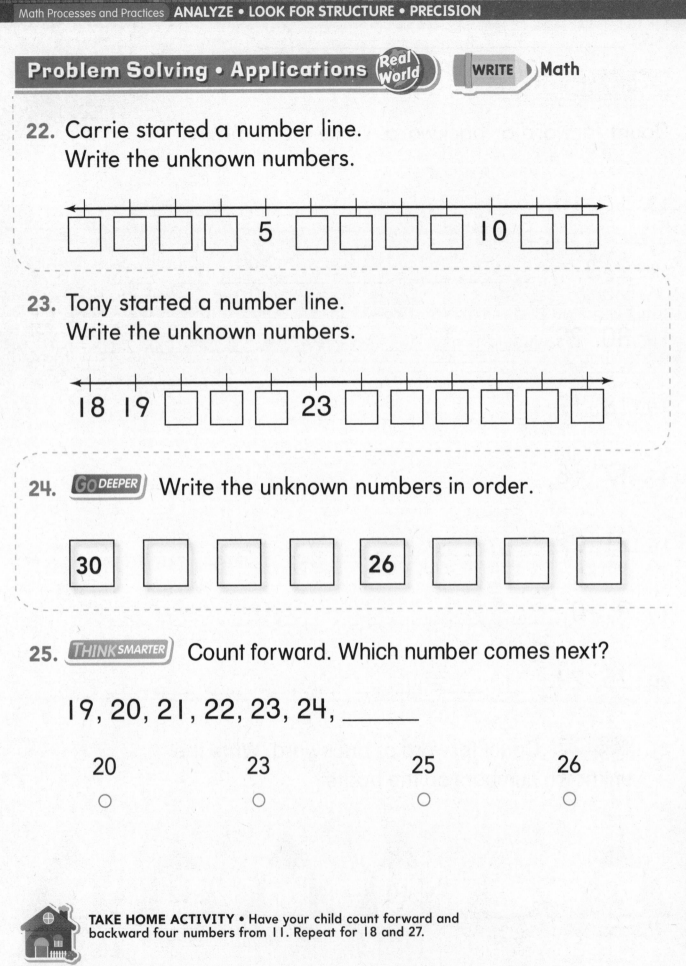

22. Carrie started a number line.
Write the unknown numbers.

☐ ☐ ☐ ☐ 5 ☐ ☐ ☐ ☐ 10 ☐ ☐

23. Tony started a number line.
Write the unknown numbers.

18 19 ☐ ☐ ☐ 23 ☐ ☐ ☐ ☐ ☐ ☐

24. Go DEEPER Write the unknown numbers in order.

30 ☐ ☐ ☐ 26 ☐ ☐ ☐

25. THINK SMARTER Count forward. Which number comes next?

19, 20, 21, 22, 23, 24, _____

20 ○   23 ○   25 ○   26 ○

TAKE HOME ACTIVITY • Have your child count forward and
backward four numbers from 11. Repeat for 18 and 27.

Count Forward and Backward by Ones

Learning Objective You will learn to count forward and backward by ones.

Count forward or backward.
Write the numbers.

1. 11, 12, ____, ____, ____, ____, ____, ____, ____, ____

2. 25, 24, ____, ____, ____, ____, ____, ____, ____, ____

3. 20, 21, ____, ____, ____, ____, ____, ____, ____, ____

4. 16, 15, ____, ____, ____, ____, ____, ____, ____, ____

5. 5, 6, ____, ____, ____, ____, ____, ____, ____, ____

6. 19, 20, ____, ____, ____, ____, ____, ____, ____, ____

7. 17, 16, ____, ____, ____, ____, ____, ____, ____, ____

8. 30, 29, ____, ____, ____, ____, ____, ____, ____, ____

Problem Solving *Real World*

9. Explain how to count forward and backward. Start at 20.

_____

_____

_____

Lesson Check

1. Which number comes next?

26, 25, 24, 23, 22, ____

27   22   21   20
○   ○   ○   ○

2. What are the unknown numbers?

18, 19, ____, 21, 22, ____

19, 20   21, 22   20, 23   24, 25
○   ○   ○   ○

Spiral Review

3. What number is the difference?

12 − 7 = ____

3   4   5   6
○   ○   ○   ○

4. What is the sum of the doubles plus one fact?

6 + 5 = ____

12   11   10   1
○   ○   ○   ○

Name _____

Skip Count by Twos, Fives, and Tens

Essential Question How does skip counting help to find the total number of objects?

Learning Objective You will skip count by twos, fives, and tens to find the total number of objects.

Listen and Draw *Real World*

You can count in different ways to find how many.

Math Talk

Math Processes and Practices ①

Does grouping the stars by 10 change the total number of stars? **Explain.**

FOR THE TEACHER • Discuss different ways to count the stars. Then have children count by ones to 10, circling sets of 10 stars as they count. Lead them to count by tens to find how many stars in all.

Model and Draw

Skip count by twos to find how many leaves.

> Add 2 to each number to get the next number.

<u>2</u> <u>4</u> <u>6</u> ___ ___

> Add 5 to each number to get the next number.

Skip count by fives to find how many petals.

<u>5</u> <u>10</u> ___ ___ ___

Skip count by tens to find how many fingers.

> Add 10 to each number to get the next number.

<u>10</u> <u>20</u> ___ ___ ___

Share and Show   MATH BOARD

Skip count to find how many.

1. <u>10</u> ___ ___ ___ ___ ___ ___ toes

2. <u>5</u> ___ ___ ___ ___ ___ ___ balloons

3. <u>2</u> ___ ___ ___ ___ ___ ___ flowers

20 twenty

Name _____

Skip count to find how many.

4.

_5_ _____ _____ _____ _____ _____ _____ flowers

5.

_10_ _____ _____ _____ _____ _____ _____ fingers

6.

_2_ _____ _____ _____ _____ _____ _____ kites

Skip count. Write the missing numbers.

7. 10, _____, 30, _____, _____, 60, 70, _____

8. 5, _____, 15, _____, 25, _____, _____ 40, _____

9. GO DEEPER Solve. Each ladybug has 5 spots.
How many spots do 6 ladybugs
have in all?

_____ spots

Problem Solving Real World   WRITE Math

10. Skip count to find how many grapes.

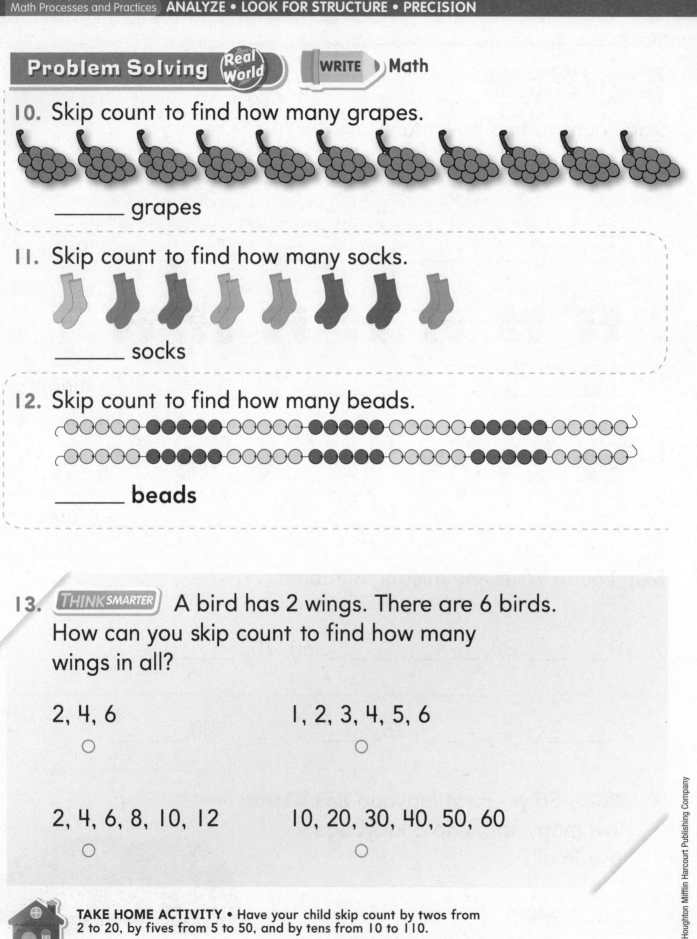

_____ grapes

11. Skip count to find how many socks.

_____ socks

12. Skip count to find how many beads.

_____ **beads**

13. THINK SMARTER   A bird has 2 wings. There are 6 birds.
How can you skip count to find how many
wings in all?

2, 4, 6   1, 2, 3, 4, 5, 6
○   ○

2, 4, 6, 8, 10, 12   10, 20, 30, 40, 50, 60
○   ○

TAKE HOME ACTIVITY • Have your child skip count by twos from
2 to 20, by fives from 5 to 50, and by tens from 10 to 110.

Skip Count by Twos, Fives, and Tens

Learning Objective You will skip count by twos, fives, and tens to find the total number of objects.

Skip count to find how many.

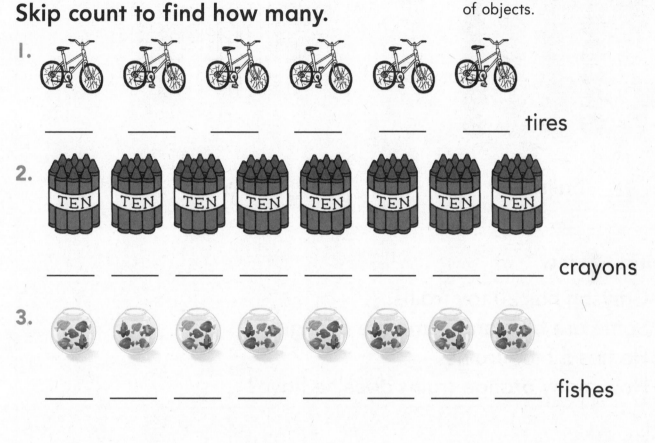

1. __ __ __ __ __ __ tires

2. __ __ __ __ __ __ __ __ crayons

3. __ __ __ __ __ __ __ __ fishes

Problem Solving Real World

4. There are 10 crayons in each box. How many crayons are in 4 boxes?

____ crayons

5. **WRITE** Math Look back at Exercise 3. What pattern do you see when you skip count by fives?

_____

Lesson Check

Skip count to find how many.

1. _____ balls

2. _____ ones

Spiral Review

3. Greyson has 20 toy trains.
   Some are blue and some are orange.
   He has 5 blue trains.
   How many orange trains does he have?

   25   20   15   5
   ○   ○   ○   ○

4. Which way makes 9?

   7 + 3   3 + 3 + 3   10 − 9   10 + 1
   ○   ○   ○   ○

Name _____

Order Sets

Essential Question How can place value help you put numbers in order?

Learning Objective You will use base ten blocks to order sets from least to greatest and greatest to least.

Listen and Draw (Real World)

Use ▭▭▭ ▪. Draw quick pictures to show the numbers. Use 🖍 to circle the number that is least. Use 🖍 to circle the number that is greatest.

_____   50   _____

Math Talk
If you look at three numbers, how can you decide which number is least? **Explain.**

 FOR THE TEACHER • Read the following aloud. Think of a number that is less than 50 and write it in the workspace on the left. Then think of a number that is greater than 50 and write it in the workspace on the right.

Use place value to put the numbers in order.

What does the 3 in 36 and 38 mean?

What does the 3 in 53 mean?

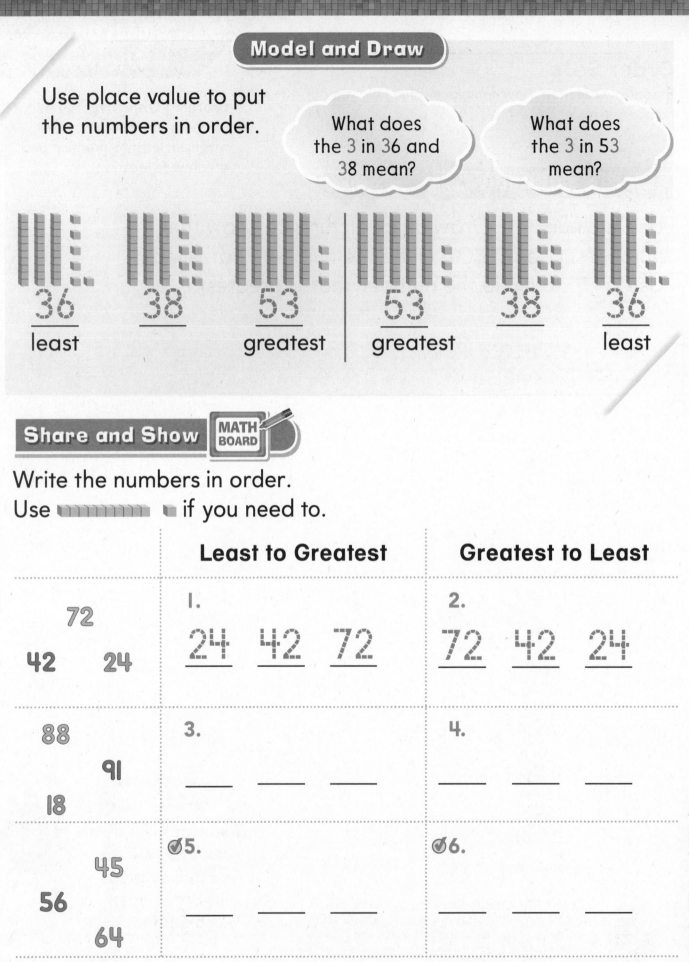

36   38   53 | 53   38   36

least   greatest | greatest   least

Share and Show MATH BOARD

Write the numbers in order.
Use ▭▭▭ if you need to.

	Least to Greatest	Greatest to Least
72 42 24	1. 24 42 72	2. 72 42 24
88 91 18	3. ___ ___ ___	4. ___ ___ ___
45 56 64	✓5. ___ ___ ___	✓6. ___ ___ ___

26 twenty-six

On Your Own

Write the numbers in order.
Use ▭▭▭▭▭ ▪ if you need to.

	Least to Greatest	Greatest to Least
67 43 76	7. 43 67 76	8. ___ ___ ___
94 29 37	9. ___ ___ ___	10. ___ ___ ___
74 82 26	11. ___ ___ ___	12. ___ ___ ___
100 63 48	13. ___ ___ ___	14. ___ ___ ___
55 52 58	15. ___ ___ ___	16. ___ ___ ___

Problem Solving • Applications Real World   WRITE Math

GO DEEPER Solve. Write the numbers in order.

17. 3 tens and 2 ones
    3 tens and 4 ones
    2 tens and 4 ones

    ___ < ___ < ___
    least   greatest

18. 6 ones and 2 tens
    1 one and 5 tens
    6 ones and 8 tens

    ___ > ___ > ___
    greatest   least

19. 7 tens and 7 ones
    4 tens and 2 ones
    6 tens and 0 ones

    ___ > ___ > ___
    greatest   least

20. 8 ones and 9 tens
    4 ones and 0 tens
    0 ones and 9 tens

    ___ < ___ < ___
    least   greatest

21. **THINK SMARTER** Which is the unknown number?

    ___   60   30
    greatest   least

    ⭘ 10   ⭘ 30   ⭘ 50   ⭘ 100

TAKE HOME ACTIVITY • Write three two-digit numbers, such as 47, 78, and 63. Have your child write the numbers in order and tell you if the order is from least to greatest or greatest to least.

Order Sets

Write the numbers in order.

	Least to Greatest	Greatest to Least
53 66 38	1. ___ ___ ___	2. ___ ___ ___
88 33 25	3. ___ ___ ___	4. ___ ___ ___
66 67 63	5. ___ ___ ___	6. ___ ___ ___
71 100 44	7. ___ ___ ___	8. ___ ___ ___
98 99 94	9. ___ ___ ___	10. ___ ___ ___

Problem Solving Real World

Solve. Write the numbers in order.

11. 1 one and 4 tens
    5 ones and 4 tens
    8 ones and 2 tens   ___ ___ ___
                          least   greatest

Lesson Check

1. Which number is least?

   ○ 91

   ○ 94

   ○ 99

   ○ 100

2. Which numbers are in order from greatest to least?

   ○ 35, 46, 74

   ○ 5, 51, 46

   ○ 74, 46, 51

   ○ 74, 51, 46

Spiral Review

3. Which is the same as 98?

   8 tens 9 ones   9 ones 8 tens   9 tens 8 ones   90 tens

   ○   ○   ○   ○

4. Circle the 4th heart.

   1st

5. Draw a square around the 9th heart.

   1st

6. Underline the 10th heart.

   1st

Name _____

Make Reasonable Estimates

Essential Question How can you solve a problem by making a reasonable estimate?

Learning Objective You will learn how to make a reasonable estimate.

Listen and Draw Real World

Look at the bowls of strawberries. Circle the bowl that has about 20 strawberries.

10 strawberries

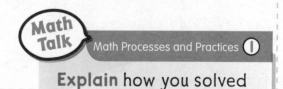

Math Talk Math Processes and Practices ①

Explain how you solved the problem.

FOR THE TEACHER • Read the following problem. Look at the bowls of strawberries. Without counting, which bowl has about 20 strawberries?

Virginia SOL Success • 7.5a

Model and Draw

THINK
Which answer makes the most sense?

An estimate is an amount that shows about how many.

About how many are there?
Circle your estimate. Explain your choice.

about 2 🍎

(about 20 🍎)

about 200 🍎

There are more than 2 apples. There are much fewer than 200 apples. There are about 20 apples.

Share and Show   MATH BOARD

✓1. About how many 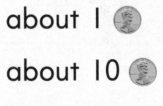 are there? Circle your estimate. Explain your choice.

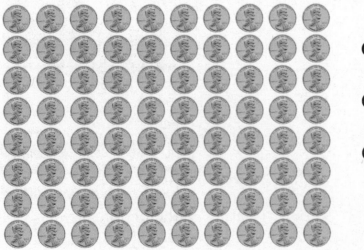

about 1 🪙

about 10 🪙

about 100 🪙

On Your Own

2. About how many 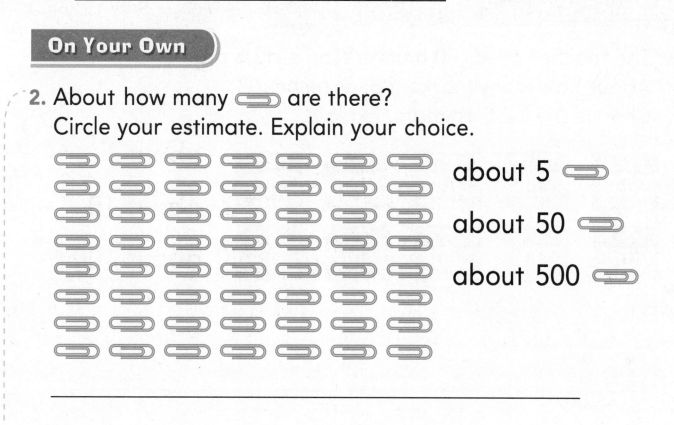 are there?
   Circle your estimate. Explain your choice.

about 5 ⊂⊃

about 50 ⊂⊃

about 500 ⊂⊃

_____

_____

3. About how many jellybeans are there?
   Circle your estimate. Explain your choice.

about 1 jellybean

about 10 jellybeans

about 100 jellybeans

_____

_____

Problem Solving • Applications (Real World)   WRITE Math

4. The teacher needs 80 markers for a class project.
About how many markers does he need?
Choose the best estimate. Explain.

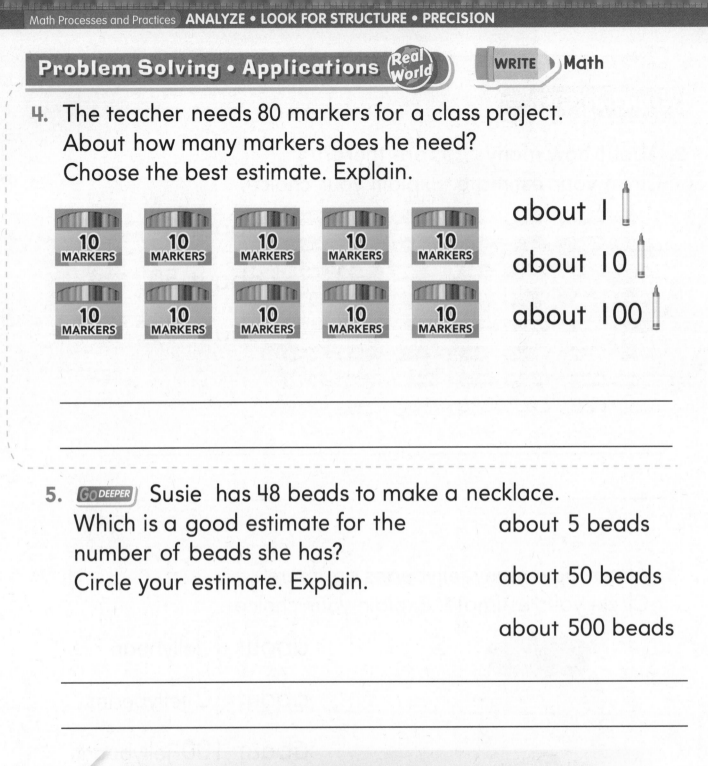

about 1

about 10

about 100

_____

_____

5. **GO DEEPER** Susie has 48 beads to make a necklace.
Which is a good estimate for the
number of beads she has?
Circle your estimate. Explain.

about 5 beads

about 50 beads

about 500 beads

_____

_____

6. **THINK SMARTER** Look at the choice you made in Exercise 4.
Count the boxes of markers by tens. Mark an X on the
actual number of boxes the teacher would need.

TAKE HOME ACTIVITY • Put 23 pennies on a table. Ask your
child to estimate the number of pennies, 2, 20, or 200. Have him
or her explain his or her answer.

Make Reasonable Estimates

Learning Objective You will solve a problem by making reasonable estimates.

1. About how many 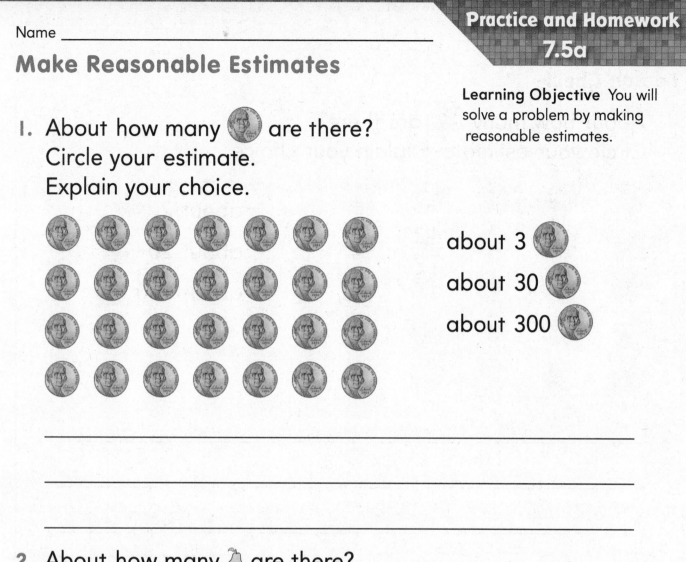 are there?
   Circle your estimate.
   Explain your choice.

about 3

about 30

about 300

_____

_____

_____

2. About how many 🍐 are there?
   Circle your estimate.
   Explain your choice.

about 1

about 10

about 100

_____

_____

Lesson Check

1. About how many 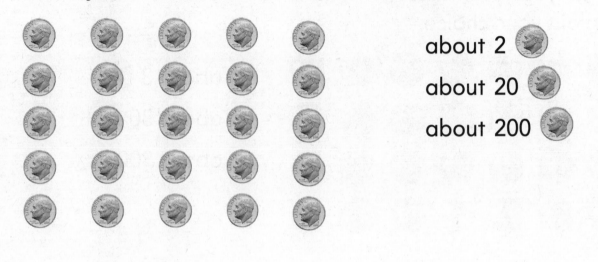 are there?
Circle your estimate. Explain your choice.

about 2

about 20

about 200

_____

_____

_____

Spiral Review

2. Which number is least?

   - ○ 91
   - ○ 94
   - ○ 99
   - ○ 100

3. Which numbers are in order from greatest to least?

   - ○ 35, 46, 74
   - ○ 35, 51, 46
   - ○ 74, 46, 51
   - ○ 74, 51, 46

Name _____

Create and Solve Addition and Subtraction Story Problems

Essential Question How can an addition or subtraction sentence help you create and solve a story problem?

Learning Objective You will create and solve addition and subtraction story problems.

Listen and Draw *Real World*

Look at the addition and subtraction facts. Draw to show a story problem. Then solve.

$4 + 3 =$ ___

$8 - 2 =$ ___

FOR THE TEACHER • Have children tell a story problem using the addition fact and the subtraction fact. Then have them use two-color counters to solve the problems. Have them draw the counters to show their work.

Math Talk
Tell your story problems to a classmate. How are your story problems alike?

Write a story problem for the subtraction
fact. Draw a picture to solve.

$5 - 3 = \underline{2}$

Meg sees 5 fish.

3 fish swim away.

How many fish are left?

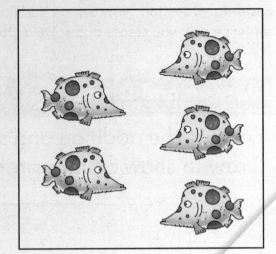

_____

Write a story problem for the addition fact.
Draw a picture to solve.

✓1. $9 + 4 = \underline{}$

Name _____

Write a story problem for the addition and subtraction facts. Draw pictures to solve.

2. 7 + 3 = ____

_____
_____
_____
_____
_____

3. 11 − 6 = ____

_____
_____
_____
_____
_____

Problem Solving • Applications (Real World)

Write a story problem for the addition and subtraction facts. Draw pictures to solve.

4. $9 - \underline{\hspace{1.5cm}} = 5$

_____

_____

_____

_____

_____

5. GO DEEPER $\underline{\hspace{1.5cm}} + \underline{\hspace{1.5cm}} = 15$

_____

_____

_____

_____

_____

6. THINK SMARTER Which addition sentence is shown?

$3 + 3 = 6$ | $5 + 3 = 8$ | $8 + 8 = 16$ | $6 + 8 = 14$
◯ | ◯ | ◯ | ◯

🏠 **TAKE HOME ACTIVITY** • Have your child write a story problem for $7 + 4$. Then have him or her draw a picture to solve the problem.

Create and Solve Addition and Subtraction Story Problems

Learning Objective You will create and solve addition and subtraction story problems.

Write a story problem for the subtraction fact. Draw a picture to solve.

1. $11 - 3 = $ ___

_____

_____

_____

_____

Problem Solving Real World

2. Write a story problem for this missing addend. Draw a picture to solve.

$$7 + \underline{} = 12$$

_____

_____

_____

_____

Lesson Check

1. Which fact matches the story?

   Jim has 8 red rocks and
   3 white rocks. How many
   rocks does Jim have?

   ○ $8 + 8 = 16$ ○ $8 - 3 = 5$

   ○ $8 + 3 = 11$ ○ $3 + 5 = 8$

2. Which fact matches the story?

   There are 7 brown birds.
   3 fly away.
   How many birds are left?

   ○ $7 - 7 = 0$ ○ $7 - 1 = 6$

   ○ $7 + 3 = 10$ ○ $7 - 3 = 4$

Spiral Review

3. What is the sum?

   $$4 + 3 = \underline{\quad}$$

   3   4   5   7
   ○   ○   ○   ○

4. What is the difference?

   $$12 - 3 = \underline{\quad}$$

   0   6   9   10
   ○   ○   ○   ○

Name _____

Measure and Compare Weights

Essential Question How do you use a balance to compare the weights of objects?

Learning Objective You will use a balance to compare weight.

Listen and Draw Real World Hands On

Use real objects, a , and cubes.
Draw to show your work.

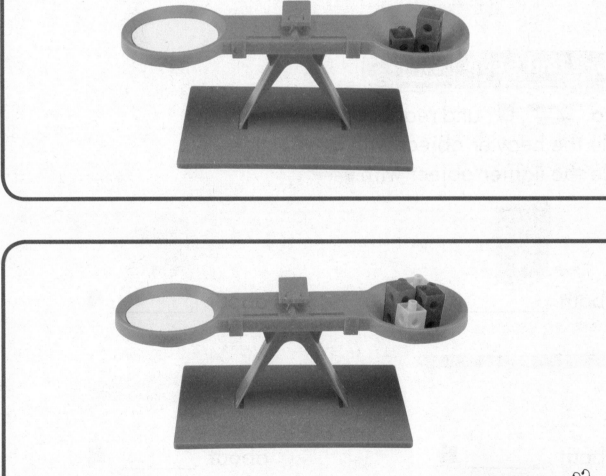

Math Talk
Explain why a different object is on each balance.

🍎 **FOR THE TEACHER** • Read the following problem. What objects can you use to balance the cubes? Have children use classroom objects to act it out.

Model and Draw

Compare. Which is heavier? Circle the 🍶 or the 🖊.

9 cubes balance this glue bottle.

6 cubes balance this glue stick.

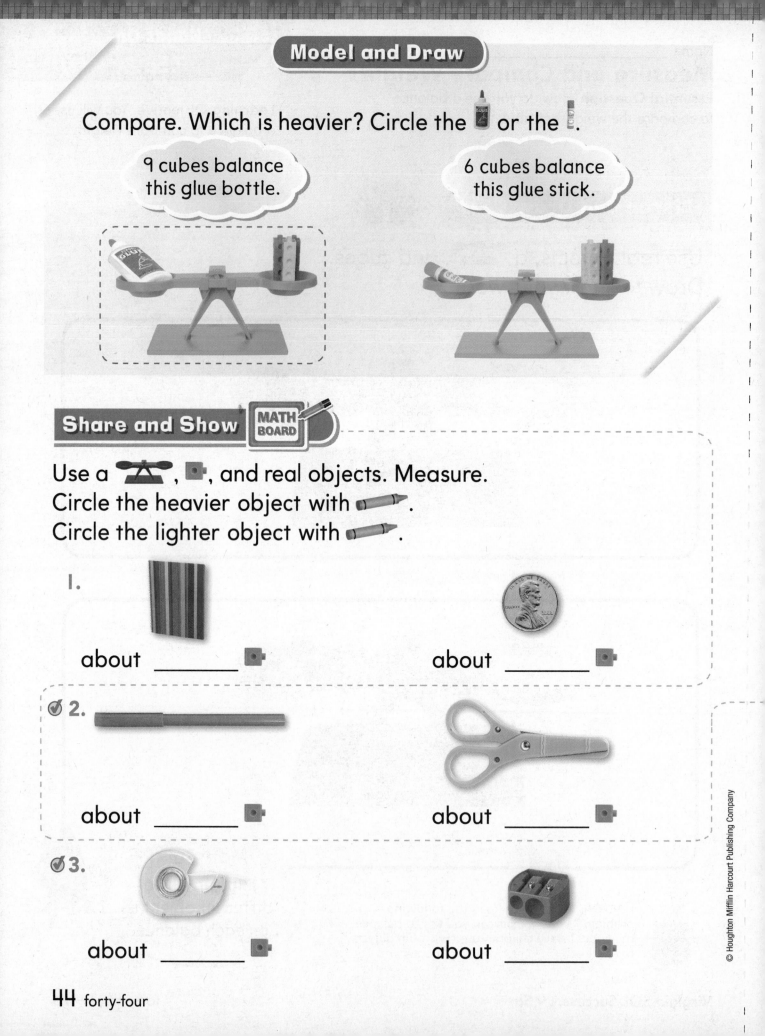

Share and Show MATH BOARD

Use a ⚖, ◼, and real objects. Measure.
Circle the heavier object with 🖍.
Circle the lighter object with 🖍.

1.

about _____ ◼   about _____ ◼

✔ 2.

about _____ ◼   about _____ ◼

✔ 3.

about _____ ◼   about _____ ◼

44 forty-four

Name _____

Group cubes to help you count.

Use a ⟨balance⟩, ⟨cube⟩, and real objects. Measure.
Circle the heavier object with ⟨crayon⟩.
Circle the lighter object with ⟨crayon⟩.

4.

about _____ ⟨cube⟩   about _____ ⟨cube⟩

5.

about _____ ⟨cube⟩   about _____ ⟨cube⟩

6.

about _____ ⟨cube⟩   about _____ ⟨cube⟩

7. Circle the heavier object with ⟨crayon⟩.
Circle the lighter object with ⟨crayon⟩.

Problem Solving • Applications Real World WRITE Math

Solve.

8. Sophie uses 5 cubes to balance her yarn. Draw an object that weighs more than 5 cubes.

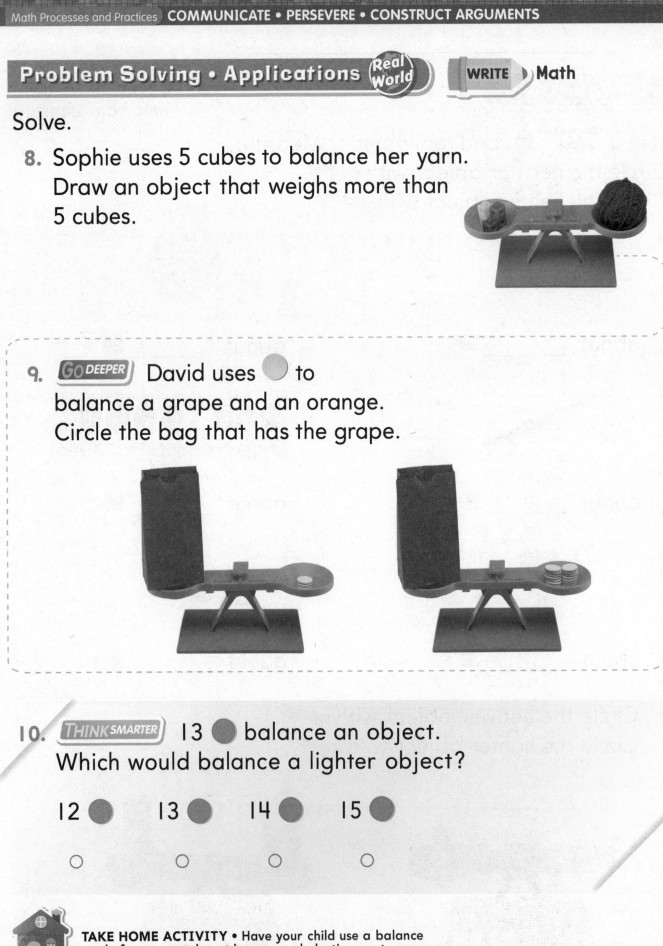

9. GO DEEPER David uses ⬤ to balance a grape and an orange. Circle the bag that has the grape.

10. THINK SMARTER 13 ⬤ balance an object. Which would balance a lighter object?

12 ⬤   13 ⬤   14 ⬤   15 ⬤

○   ○   ○   ○

🏠 **TAKE HOME ACTIVITY** • Have your child use a balance made from a metal coat hanger and plastic cups to compare the weights of two objects in your home.

Measure and Compare Weights

Learning Objective You will use a balance to compare weights.

Use a 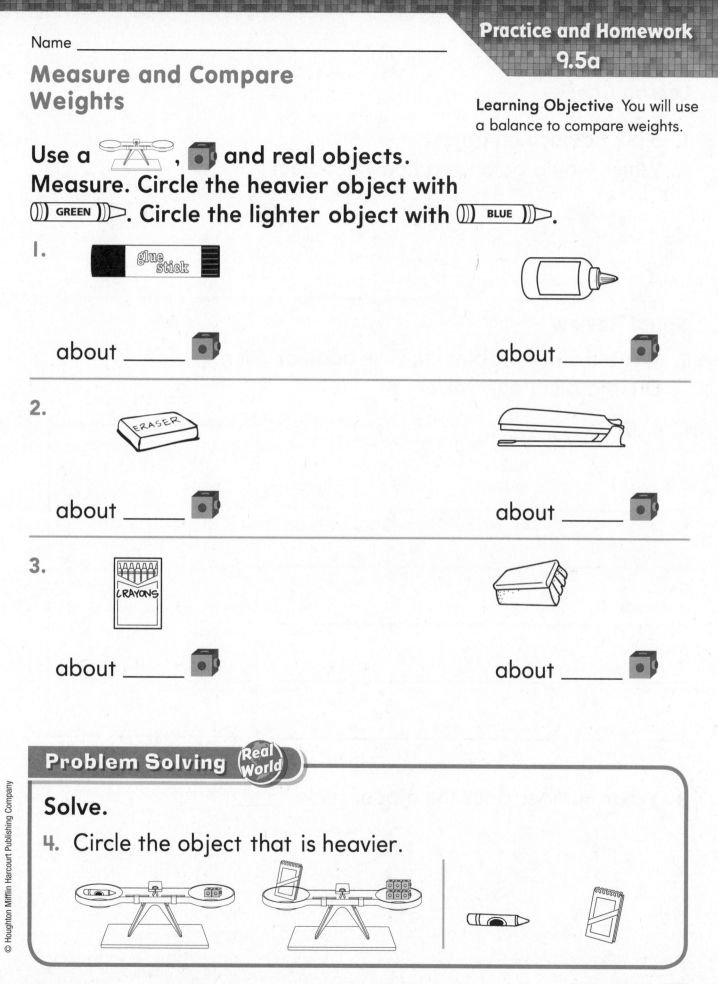 , and real objects.
Measure. Circle the heavier object with
GREEN . Circle the lighter object with BLUE .

1.

glue stick

about _____

about _____

2.

ERASER

about _____

about _____

3.

CRAYONS

about _____

about _____

Problem Solving Real World

Solve.

4. Circle the object that is heavier.

Lesson Check

1. 6 🎲 balance an object.
   Which would balance a heavier object?

   7 🎲   6 🎲   5 🎲   4 🎲

   ○   ○   ○   ○

Spiral Review

2. Write a story problem for the addition fact.
   Draw a picture to solve.

   8 + 4 = _____

   _____

   _____

   _____

   _____

3. What number does the model show? _____

Measure and Compare Volumes

Essential Question How do you measure and compare volume of containers?

Learning Objective You will measure and compare the volume of containers.

Listen and Draw

Use objects to show the problem. Draw to show your work.

holds **more**   holds **less**

FOR THE TEACHER • Read the problem. Have children use classroom objects to act it out. Rami has a mug. He wants to find a container that holds more than the mug and a container that holds less than the mug. What containers might he find?

Math Talk
How do you know which container holds more? **Explain.**

Model and Draw

The mug is filled with rice.
Draw a container that holds more
than 20  of rice.
Write the measurement.

Volume is the amount a container can hold.

about 20    about _____

Share and Show MATH BOARD

Use a , rice, and real objects.
Measure. Then circle the container that
holds more.

	Object	Measurement
1.		about _____ 🥄
		about _____ 🥄
✓ 2.	YOGURT	about _____ 🥄
		about _____ 🥄

50 fifty

© Houghton Mifflin Harcourt Publishing Company

On Your Own

Use a 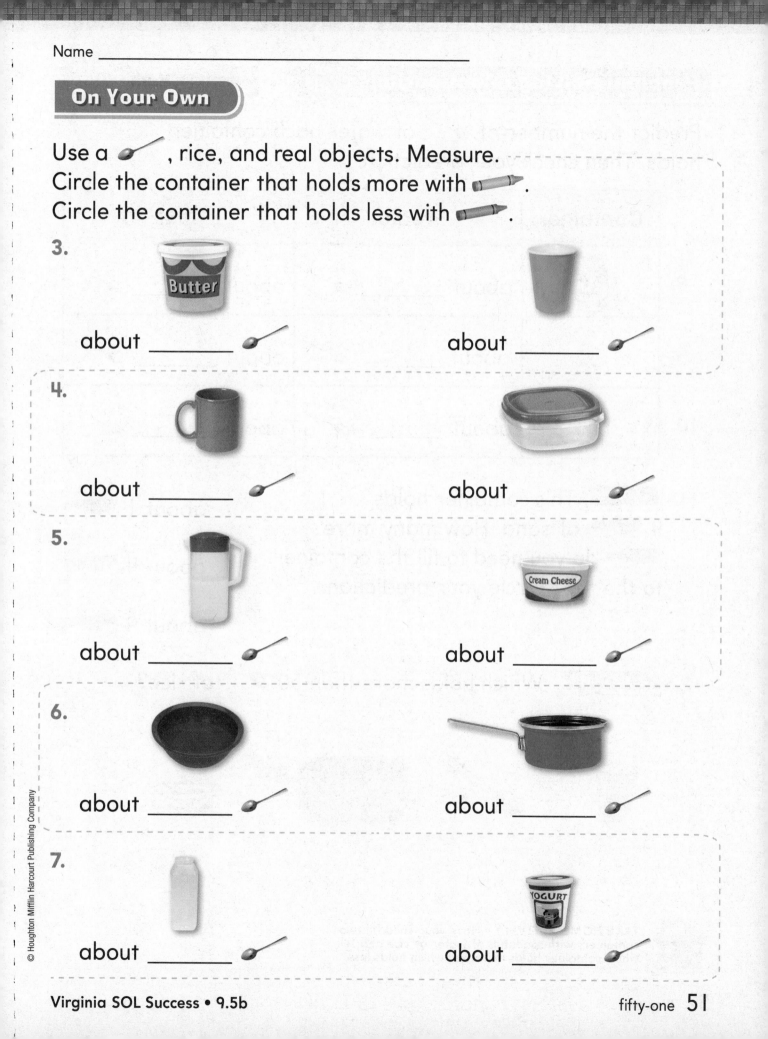 , rice, and real objects. Measure.
Circle the container that holds more with ✏.
Circle the container that holds less with ✏.

3.

about _____ 🥄   about _____ 🥄

4.

about _____ 🥄   about _____ 🥄

5.

about _____ 🥄   about _____ 🥄

6.

about _____ 🥄   about _____ 🥄

7.

about _____ 🥄   about _____ 🥄

Problem Solving • Applications (Real World)    WRITE Math

Predict the number of 🥄 of water each container holds. Then check your prediction.

	Container	Predict	Test
8.	MILK	about _____ 🥄	about _____ 🥄
9.	bottle	about _____ 🥄	about _____ 🥄
10.	COTTAGE CHEESE	about _____ 🥄	about _____ 🥄

11. GO DEEPER This container holds 4 🥄 of sand. How many more 🥄 do you need to fill the container to the top? Circle your prediction.

about 1 🥄

about 4 🥄

about 9 🥄

12. THINK SMARTER Which holds more than 50 🥄 of rice?

○   ○   ○   ○

TAKE HOME ACTIVITY • Have your child fill two containers with spoonfuls of water or rice and tell which container holds more and which holds less.

© Houghton Mifflin Harcourt Publishing Company

Measure and Compare Volumes

Use a 🥄 , rice, and real objects.
Measure. Circle the container that holds
more with ▭ RED ▭. Circle the container
that holds less with ▭ BLUE ▭.

Learning Objective You will
measure and compare the
volume of containers.

1.

about _____ 🥄   about _____ 🥄

2.

about _____ 🥄   about _____ 🥄

3.

about _____ 🥄   about _____ 🥄

Problem Solving Real World

Solve.

4. Logan fills a bucket with water.

Nick fills a cup with water.
Who has the container
that holds more water?   _____

Lesson Check

1. Which holds more than 30 ⌒ of rice?

○   ○   ○   ○

2. Which holds less than 5 ⌒ of rice?

○   ○   ○   ○

Spiral Review

3. Use doubles to find the sum of 6 + 7.
   Write the number sentence.

   _____ + _____ + _____ = _____

4. Which is the unknown number?

   _____   ___70___   ___40___
   greatest   least

   20   30   60   90

   ○   ○   ○   ○

Name _____

Read a Calendar

Essential Question How does a calendar show time and help you locate dates?

Learning Objective You will find days and dates on a calendar.

 **Listen and Draw** *Real World*

This is a calendar.
Days, weeks, and months show time on a calendar.

May

Sunday	Monday	Tuesday	Wednesday	Thursday	Friday	Saturday
1	2	3	4	5	6	7
8	9	10	11	12	13	14
15	16	17	18	19	20	21
22	23	24	25	26	27	28
29	30	31				

Math Talk Math Processes and Practices ①

How did you know which dates were on Saturday? **Explain.**

FOR THE TEACHER • Read the following problem. Isabella has baseball practice every Saturday in May. Use green to color the dates Isabella will have baseball practice. Name the dates Isabella will go to baseball practice.

Virginia SOL Success • 9.9a

A calendar shows time.

Today is August 4.
Tomorrow will be August 5.
Yesterday was August 3.

Use the dates above.
Circle today. Draw a
triangle on tomorrow.
Put an X on yesterday.

August						
Sunday	Monday	Tuesday	Wednesday	Thursday	Friday	Saturday
	1	2	3	4	5	6
7	8	9	10	11	12	13
14	15	16	17	18	19	20
21	22	23	24	25	26	27
28	29	30	31			

Share and Show

Use the calendar above to answer the questions. the

1. How many Tuesdays are in this month?

   _____

2. What day of the week is August 7?

   _____

3. What date is the first Saturday?

   _____

4. Today is the 18th. What day of
   the week was yesterday?

   _____

Name _____

Use the calendar to answer the questions.

November

Sunday	Monday	Tuesday	Wednesday	Thursday	Friday	Saturday
		1	2	3	4	5
6	7	8	9	10	11	12
13	14	15	16	17	18	19
20	21	22	23	24	25	26
27	28	29	30			

5. How many Fridays are in this month?

_____

6. Today is November 4. What day of the week is tomorrow?

_____

7. Yesterday was November 12. What date is today?

_____

8. **GO DEEPER** Are there more Tuesdays or Sundays in this month?

_____

Problem Solving • Applications Real World

Use the calendar to answer the questions.

JUNE						
Sunday	Monday	Tuesday	Wednesday	Thursday	Friday	Saturday
	1	2	3	4	5	6

9. Tomorrow is June 4. What day is today?

   _____

10. June starts on what day of the week?

   _____

11. Yesterday was the first Tuesday of June.
    What date is today?

   _____

12. What is the date of the first Sunday in this month?

   _____

13. THINKSMARTER   Today is June 22. Yesterday was a Sunday.
    What day of the week is tomorrow?

   Sunday   Monday   Tuesday   Wednesday
     ○   ○   ○   ○

TAKE HOME ACTIVITY • Have your child draw pictures to describe
4 favorite days of the year and label each picture with a date. Then
help him or her put the dates in order. Finally ask your child to
identify which dates have passed and which are still to come.

Read a Calendar

Use the calendar to answer the questions.

Learning Objective You will locate days and dates on a calendar.

March

Sunday	Monday	Tuesday	Wednesday	Thursday	Friday	Saturday
			1	2	3	4
5	6	7	8	9	10	11
12	13	14	15	16	17	18
19	20	21	22	23	24	25
26	27	28	29	30	31	

1. How many Wednesdays are in this month? _____

2. Today is March 14. What day of the week was yesterday?

   _____

3. What date is the Thursday after the 17th?

   _____

4. Tomorrow is March 28. What date is today?

   _____

Problem Solving · Real World

5. Austin went fishing on the third Saturday of March. What is that? _____

Lesson Check

Use the calendar to answer the questions.

1. Today is December 19. What date is tomorrow?

   _____

2. Yesterday was December 3. What day of the week is today?

   _____

Spiral Review

3. Which number comes next?

   31, 32, 33, _____

   ○ 32

   ○ 34

   ○ 35

   ○ 43

4. Which number is greater than 15?

   ○ 1

   ○ 5

   ○ 10

   ○ 20

Name _____

Pennies, Nickels, and Dimes

Essential Question What are the values of a penny, a nickel, and a dime?

Learning Objective You will find the values of pennies, nickels, and dimes.

Listen and Draw *Real World*

Draw (1¢) to show Jerry's coins.

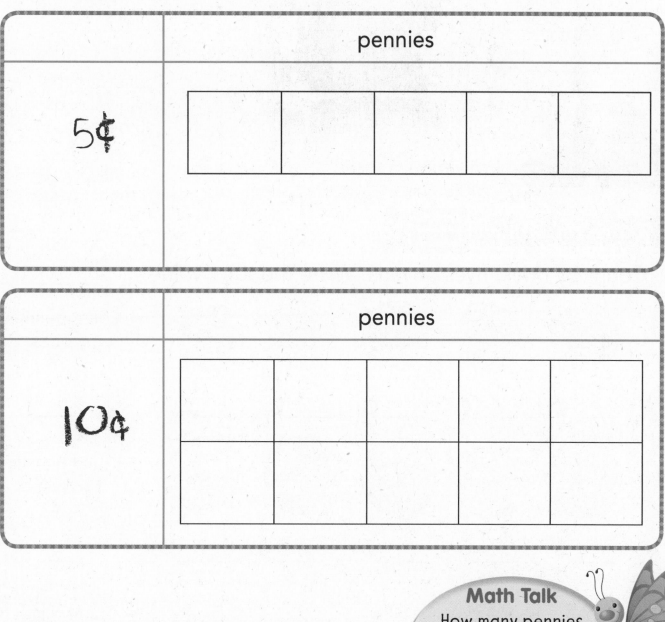

5¢	pennies

10¢	pennies

FOR THE TEACHER • Jerry knows a penny has a value of 1 cent. He wants to buy a toy that costs 5 cents. Draw the pennies. He buys another toy that costs 10 cents. Draw the pennies.

Math Talk
How many pennies would Jerry need if 2 toys cost 5 cents? **Explain.**

Model and Draw

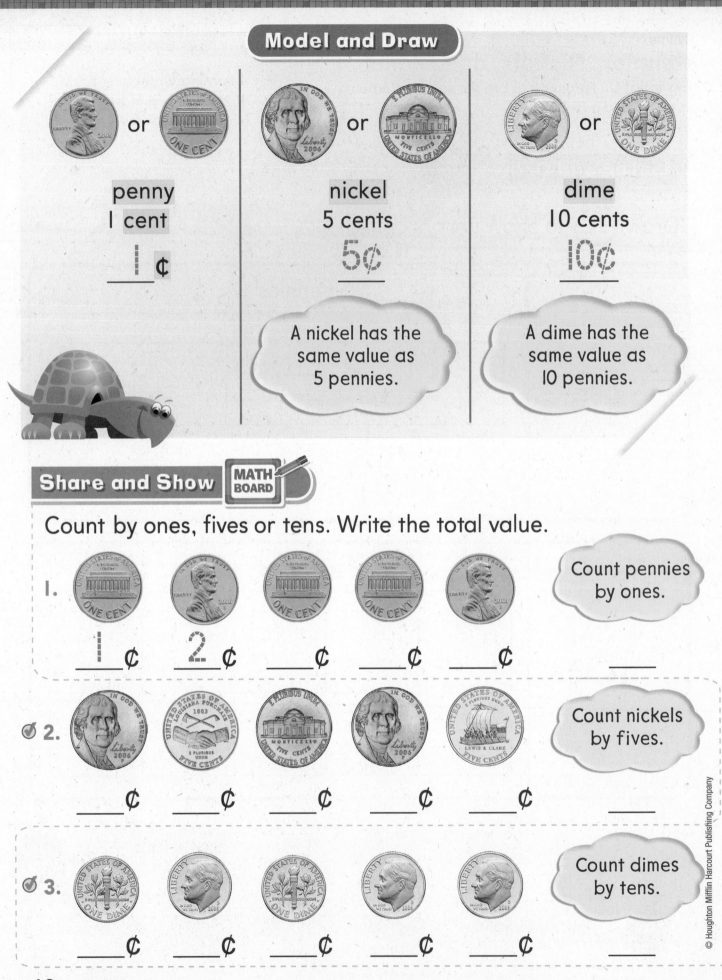

penny
1 cent

__1__ ¢

nickel
5 cents

__5¢__

A nickel has the
same value as
5 pennies.

dime
10 cents

__10¢__

A dime has the
same value as
10 pennies.

Share and Show MATH BOARD

Count by ones, fives or tens. Write the total value.

1.   __1__ ¢   __2__ ¢   ____ ¢   ____ ¢   ____ ¢   ____

Count pennies
by ones.

2.   ____ ¢   ____ ¢   ____ ¢   ____ ¢   ____ ¢   ____

Count nickels
by fives.

3.   ____ ¢   ____ ¢   ____ ¢   ____ ¢   ____ ¢   ____

Count dimes
by tens.

On Your Own

Count by ones, fives, or tens.
Write the total value.

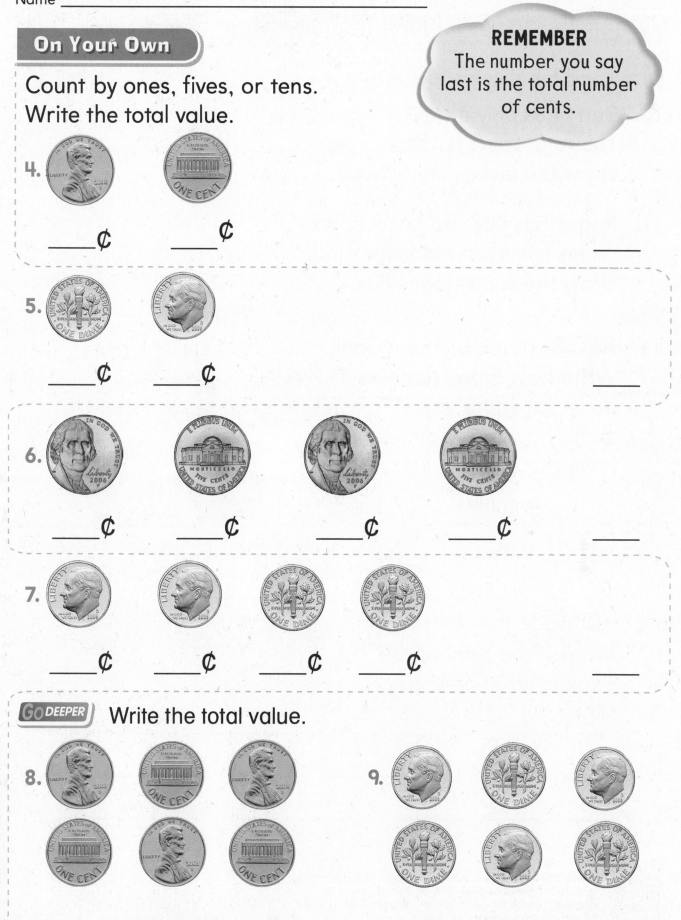

4. _____¢   _____¢   _____

5. _____¢   _____¢   _____

6. _____¢   _____¢   _____¢   _____¢   _____

7. _____¢   _____¢   _____¢   _____¢   _____

Go DEEPER   Write the total value.

8. _____   9. _____

Problem Solving • Applications

WRITE Math

Draw and label coins to solve.

10. Betty has only nickels.
    The total value is 15¢.
    Draw the nickels Betty has.

11. Roger has 40¢. He has 4 coins.
    All his coins are the same kind.
    Draw the coins Roger has.

12. **GoDEEPER** Look at the nickels.
    Write how many pennies
    have the same value.
    Write how many dimes
    have the same value.

    _____ pennies

    _____ dimes

13. **THINKSMARTER**

    What is the total value?
    Explain how you know.

    _____

    _____

    _____

 TAKE HOME ACTIVITY • Give your child different
groups of pennies. Ask him or her to count to find
the total value of each group. Repeat with groups
of nickels and groups of dimes.

Name _____

Pennies, Nickels, and Dimes
Count by ones, fives, or tens. Write the total value.

Learning Objective You will find the values of pennies, nickels, and dimes.

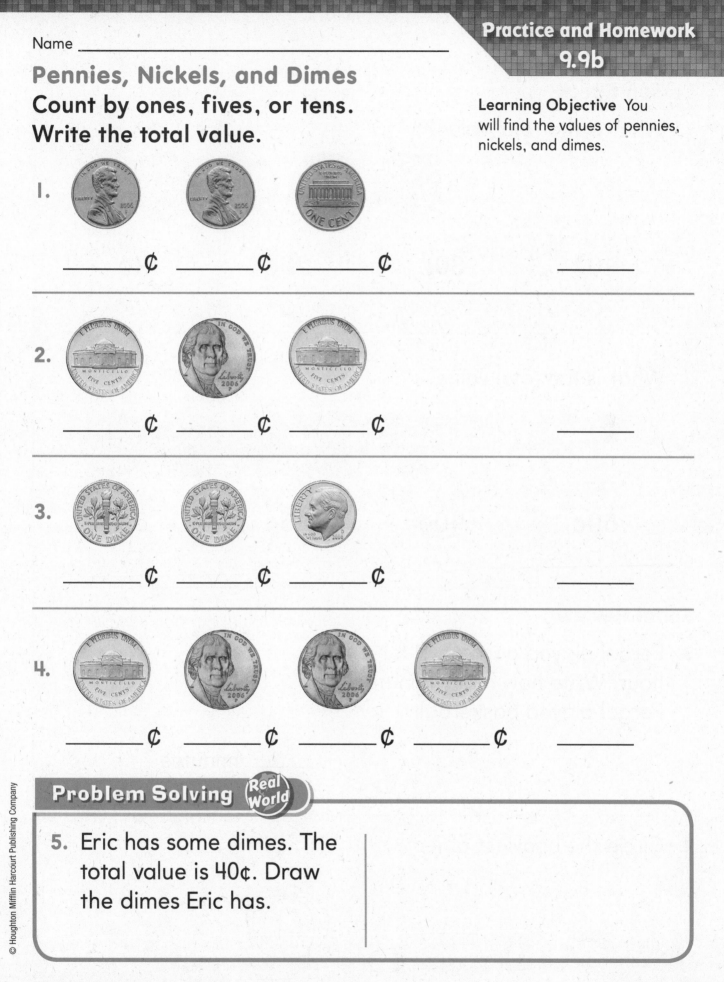

1. _____ ¢   _____ ¢   _____ ¢   _____

2. _____ ¢   _____ ¢   _____ ¢   _____

3. _____ ¢   _____ ¢   _____ ¢   _____

4. _____ ¢   _____ ¢   _____ ¢   _____ ¢

Problem Solving Real World

5. Eric has some dimes. The total value is 40¢. Draw the dimes Eric has.

Lesson Check

1. What is the total value?

40¢	30¢	20¢	4¢
○	○	○	○

2. What is the total value?

50¢	40¢	25¢	5¢
○	○	○	○

Spiral Review

3. Fergal played basketball for one hour. Write how many minutes Fergal played basketball.

_____ minutes

4. Circle the heaviest object.

Name _____

Object Graphs

Essential Question How can you use object graphs to organize and compare data?

Learning Objective You will make object graphs to organize and compare data.

Listen and Draw Real World

Toss counters. Sort by color.

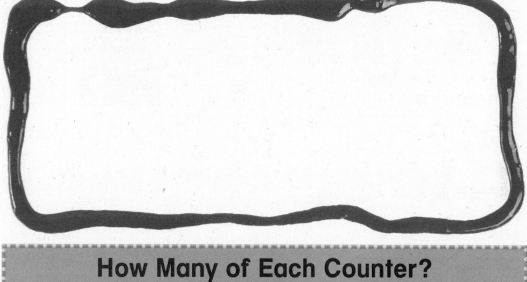

How Many of Each Counter?

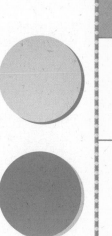

FOR THE TEACHER • Tell children the following. Toss some counters on the workspace. Sort the counters. Tell your classmate how you sorted the counters. Move the counters to the graph. Draw and color the counters.

Math Talk Math Processes and Practices ①

Explain how the graph of your classmate is alike and different from your graph.

Model and Draw

An **object** graph uses real objects to compare information.

The cubes are sorted by color.

The graph shows cubes by color.

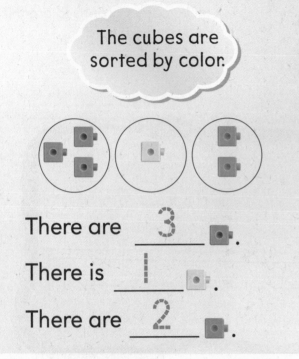

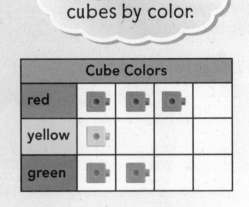

Cube Colors				
red	◙	◙	◙	
yellow	◙			
green	◙	◙		

There are ___3___ ◙.

There is ___1___ ◙.

There are ___2___ ◙.

Share and Show MATH BOARD

Sort some tiles. Make an object graph.
Draw and color each tile where it belongs.

Tile Colors						
red						
yellow						
green						

How many of each color?

1. ▮ _____   ⊘2. ▢ _____   ⊘3. ▮ _____

Name _____

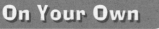 **On Your Own**

Sort some cubes. Make an object graph.
Draw and color each cube where it belongs.

Cube Colors				
■ blue				
■ green				
■ orange				
■ yellow				

How many of each color?

4. yellow _____   5. green _____

6. blue _____   7. orange _____

8. **GO DEEPER** Matthew makes a table of his trains.
Then he makes an object graph.
How many trains are on his
object graph?

_____ trains

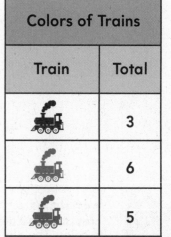

Colors of Trains	
Train	Total
🚂	3
🚂	6
🚂	5

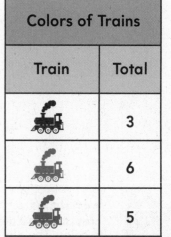

Problem Solving • Applications  WRITE Math

9. Use the table. Make an object graph.
Draw the objects where they belong.

Crayon Colors					
orange					
blue					
green					
purple					

Colors of Crayons	
Color	Number
ORANGE	3
BLUE	5
GREEN	2
PURPLE	3

10. THINK SMARTER Mya makes an object graph.
There are more yellow squares than blue circles.
There are more pink hearts than yellow squares.
There are fewer green triangles than blue circles.

Which object has the longest row on the object graph?

○   ○   ○   ○

Name ______________________________

Practice and Homework
10.0a

Hands On • Object Graphs

Learning Objective You will make object graphs to organize and compare data.

Use the table. Make an object graph. Draw the objects where they belong.

Favorite Shapes					
●					
■					
▲					
◆					

Favorite Shapes	
Shape	**Total**
●	4
■	2
▲	3
◆	5

How many of each shape?

1. ● ________ **2.** ■ ________

3. ▲ ________ **4.** ◆ ________

Problem Solving (Real World)

5. Austin made an object graph with 10 balloons. The balloons are purple, green, and yellow. There are 3 purple and 5 green balloons. How many yellow balloons are on the graph?

________ yellow balloons

6. WRITE Math Explain what the longest row in a graph shows.

____

Lesson Check

1. Use the table. Make an object graph.
   Draw the objects where they belong.

Star Colors				
★ black				
★ gray				
☆ white				

Stars	
Color	Total
black	4
gray	2
white	4

How many stars of each color?

2. black _____   3. gray _____   4. white _____

Spiral Review

5. Yesterday was June 10. What date is tomorrow?

   June 9   June 11   June 12   June 13
     ○   ○   ○   ○

6. Skip count to find how many.

_____ _____ _____ _____ _____ crayons

Sort and Classify Objects

Essential Question How can you sort and classify objects into sets?

Learning Objective You will sort and classify objects into sets.

© Houghton Mifflin Harcourt Publishing Company

Listen and Draw Real World

Shapes can be sorted different ways.

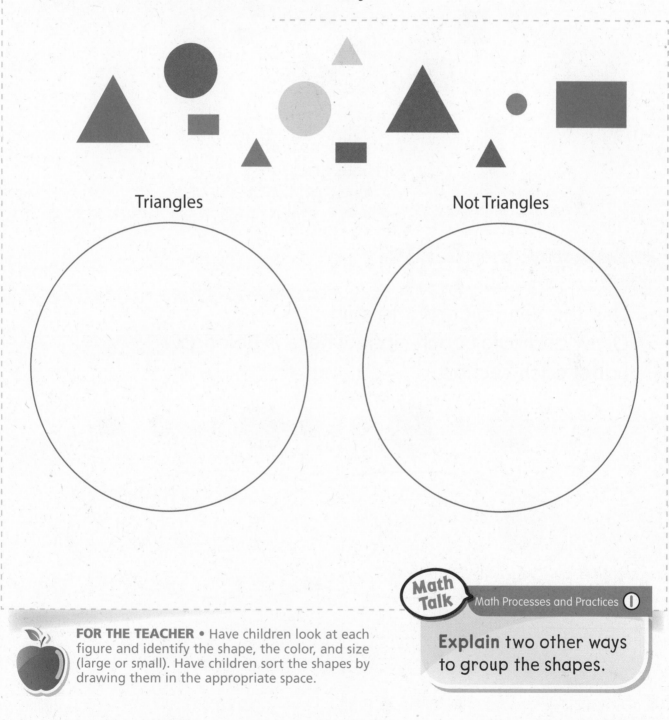

Triangles

Not Triangles

FOR THE TEACHER • Have children look at each figure and identify the shape, the color, and size (large or small). Have children sort the shapes by drawing them in the appropriate space.

Math Talk Math Processes and Practices ①

Explain two other ways to group the shapes.

Virginia SOL Success • 12.0a

seventy-three 73

A **Venn diagram** shows how things are different and alike.

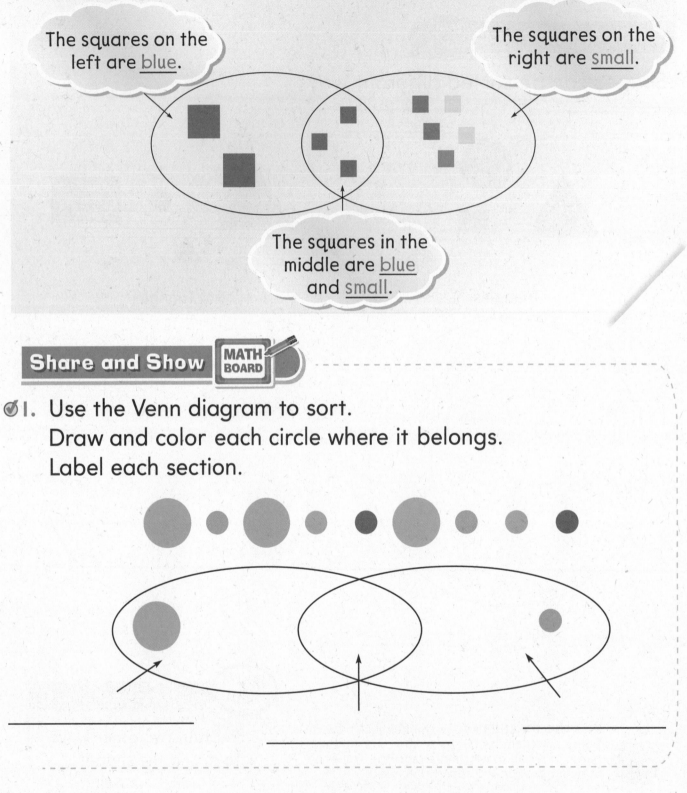

The squares on the left are <u>blue</u>.

The squares on the right are <u>small</u>.

The squares in the middle are <u>blue</u> and <u>small</u>.

Share and Show MATH BOARD

1. Use the Venn diagram to sort.
Draw and color each circle where it belongs.
Label each section.

_____   _____   _____

Name _____

On Your Own

2. Use the Venn diagram to sort.
   Draw and color each triangle where it belongs.
   Label each section.

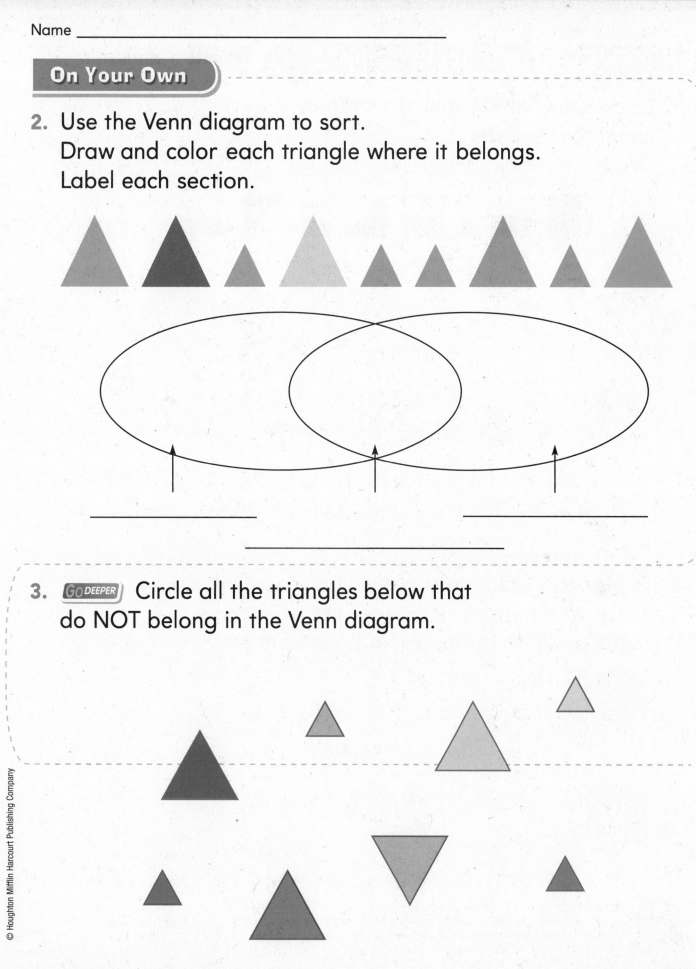

3. **GO DEEPER** Circle all the triangles below that
   do NOT belong in the Venn diagram.

Problem Solving • Applications (Real World) WRITE Math

4. Decide how to the sort the shapes.
Label the sections.
Draw the shapes where they belong.

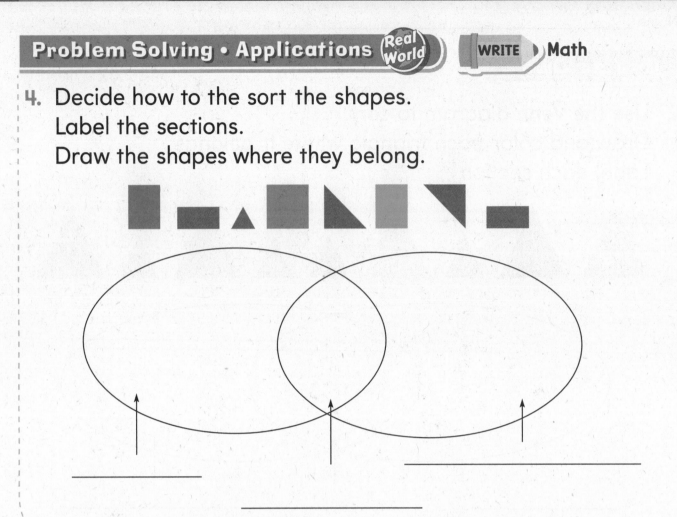

_____   _____

_____

5. THINK SMARTER Madison sorts her buttons. One set
has square buttons. The other set has purple
buttons. Which button could be in both sets?

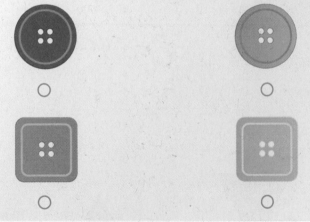

TAKE HOME ACTIVITY • Give your child a number of items,
such as small red paper clips and large multicolored paper clips
including red. Have your child sort the paper clips in a Venn
diagram.

Sort and Classify Objects

Learning Objective You will sort and classify objects into sets.

1. Draw and color each shape where it belongs. Label each section gray squares, small squares, or small gray squares.

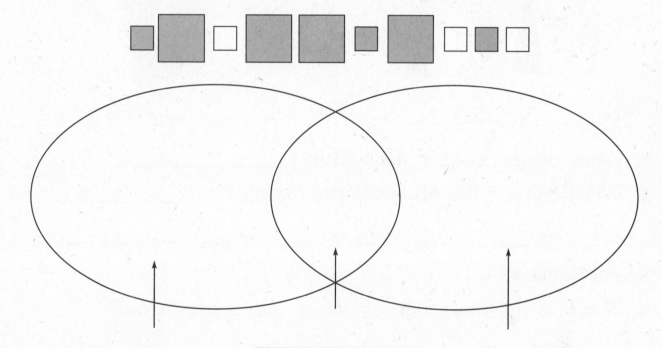

_____   _____   _____

Problem Solving (Real World)

2. Circle the object that belongs in the middle section.

3. WRITE ▸ Math Explain what objects go in the middle section of a Venn diagram.

_____

Lesson Check

1. Draw and color one object that goes in the middle.

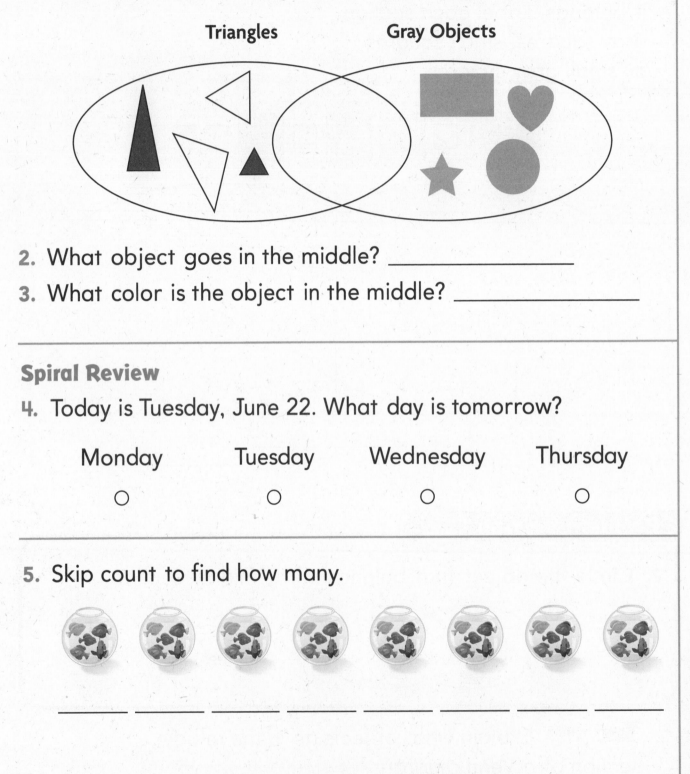

Triangles   Gray Objects

2. What object goes in the middle? _____
3. What color is the object in the middle? _____

Spiral Review

4. Today is Tuesday, June 22. What day is tomorrow?

   Monday   Tuesday   Wednesday   Thursday
      ○   ○   ○   ○

5. Skip count to find how many.

____ ____ ____ ____ ____ ____ ____ ____

Name _____

Angles in Two-Dimensional Shapes

Essential Question How do you find and count angles in two-dimensional shapes?

Learning Objective You will identify angles in two-dimensional shapes.

Listen and Draw *Real World*

Draw two different triangles.
Then draw two different rectangles.

Math Talk Math Processes and Practices

Describe a triangle and a rectangle. Tell about their sides and vertices.

FOR THE TEACHER • Have children use pencils and rulers (or other straight edges) to draw the shapes. Have them draw two different triangles in the green box and two different rectangles in the purple box.

© Houghton Mifflin Harcourt Publishing Company

Virginia SOL Success • 12.2a

When two sides of a shape meet, they form an **angle**.

angle

This shape has __3__ angles.

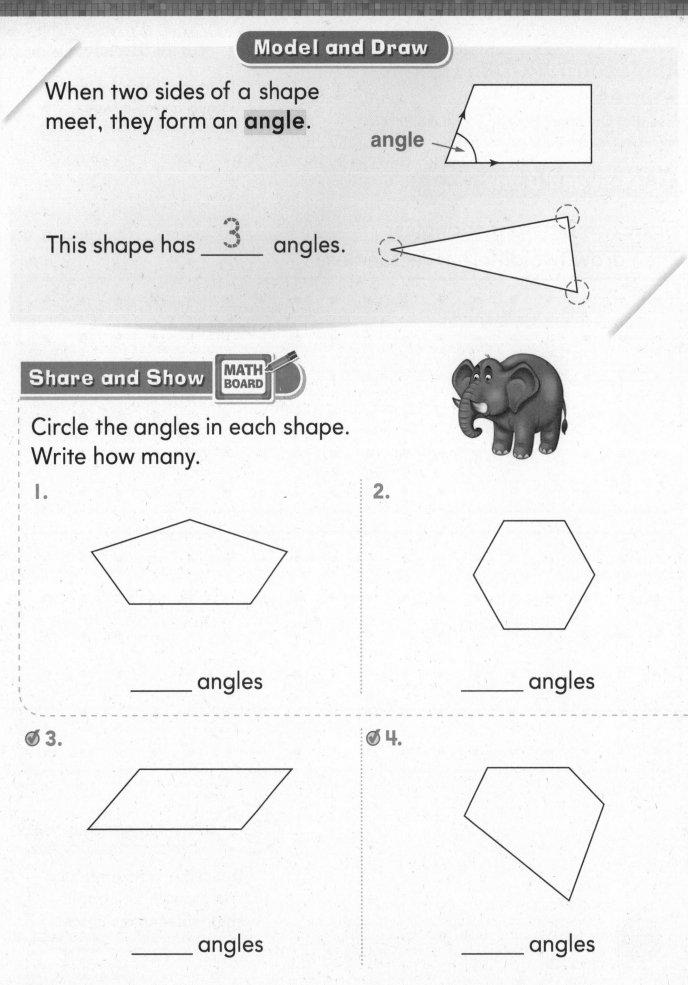

Share and Show | MATH BOARD

Circle the angles in each shape.
Write how many.

1.

_____ angles

2.

_____ angles

☑ 3.

_____ angles

☑ 4.

_____ angles

Name _____

On Your Own

Circle the angles in each shape. Write how many.

5.

_____ angles

6.

_____ angles

7.

_____ angles

8.

_____ angles

9. **THINK SMARTER** Draw more sides to make the shape. Write how many angles.

square

_____ angles

triangle

_____ angles

Problem Solving • Applications (Real World) WRITE Math

10. Draw two shapes that have 7 angles in all.

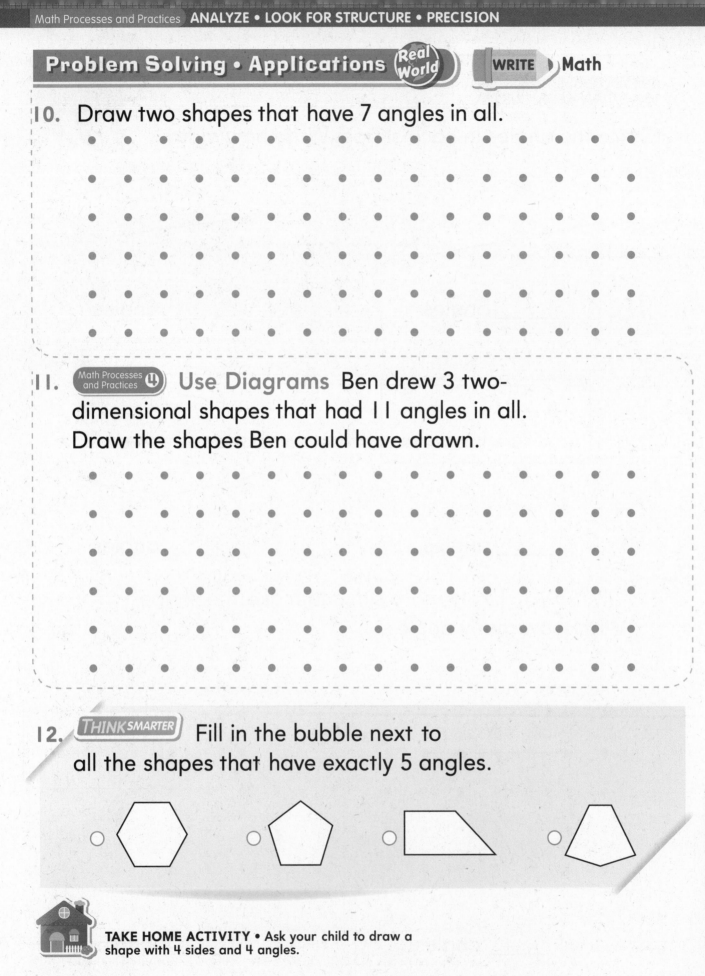

11. Math Processes and Practices 4 Use Diagrams Ben drew 3 two-dimensional shapes that had 11 angles in all. Draw the shapes Ben could have drawn.

12. THINK SMARTER Fill in the bubble next to all the shapes that have exactly 5 angles.

○   ○   ○   ○

TAKE HOME ACTIVITY • Ask your child to draw a shape with 4 sides and 4 angles.

Angles in Two-Dimensional Shapes

Learning Objective You will identify angles in two-dimensional shapes.

Circle the angles in each shape. Write how many.

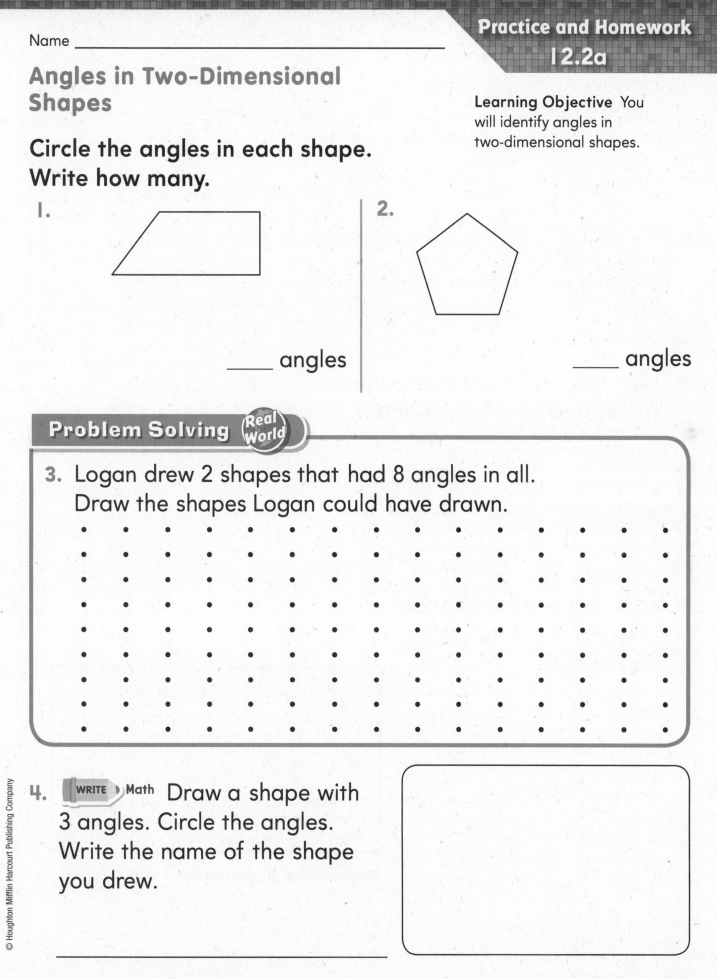

1.

_____ angles

2.

_____ angles

Problem Solving Real World

3. Logan drew 2 shapes that had 8 angles in all. Draw the shapes Logan could have drawn.

4. WRITE Math Draw a shape with 3 angles. Circle the angles. Write the name of the shape you drew.

_____

Lesson Check

1. How many angles does this shape have?

_____ angles

2. How many angles does this shape have?

_____ angles

Spiral Review

3. Use ⬭. Kevin measures the ribbon with ⬭. About how long is the ribbon?

about _____ ⬭

4. Look at the picture graph. How many children chose daisies?

_____ children

Favorite Flower					
roses	☺	☺	☺	☺	
tulips	☺	☺	☺		
daisies	☺	☺	☺	☺	☺
lilies	☺	☺			

Key: Each ☺ stands for 1 child.

Name _____

Problem Solving • Equal Shares

Essential Question How can drawing a diagram help you solve problems about equal shares?

Learning Objective You will draw a diagram to help you solve a problem.

There are two sandwiches. They are the same size. Each sandwich is cut into fourths in a different way. How might the two sandwiches be cut?

Unlock the Problem (Real World)

What do I need to find?

how the sandwiches
could be out

What information do I need to use?

There are _____ sandwiches.
Each sandwich is cut into _____.

Show how to solve the problem.

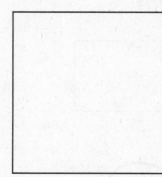

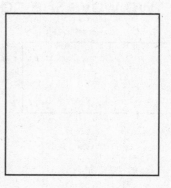

HOME CONNECTION • Your child drew a diagram to represent and solve a problem about dividing a whole in different ways to show equal shares.

© Houghton Mifflin Harcourt Publishing Company

Solve. Draw to show your answer.

1. Marquis has two sheets of paper.
   They are the same size. He wants
   to cut each sheet into halves.
   What are two ways he can cut the
   paper?

• What do I need to
  find?
• What information
  do I need to use?

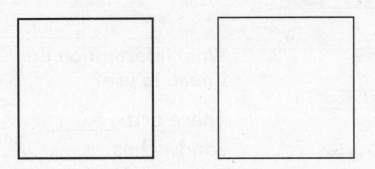

2. Shanice has two pieces of cloth.
   The pieces are the same size.
   She needs to cut each piece into fourths.
   What are two ways she can cut the cloth?

Math Talk

Math Processes and Practices ①

Look at Problem 2. How
are the cloths alike?
How are they different.
Explain.

Share and Show MATH BOARD

Solve. Draw to show your answer.

3. Brandon has two pieces of toast.
   The pieces are the same size.
   What are two ways he can cut the toast into halves?

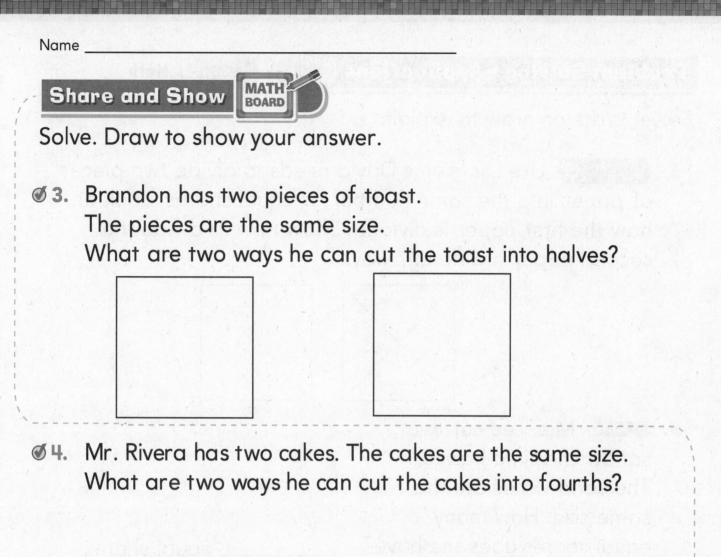

4. Mr. Rivera has two cakes. The cakes are the same size.
   What are two ways he can cut the cakes into fourths?

5. THINK SMARTER Erin has two napkins that are the same size.
   What are two ways to fold the napkins in half?

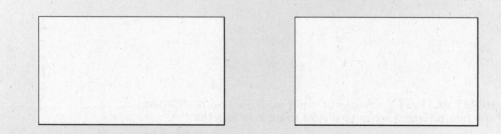

Problem Solving • Applications    WRITE   Math

Solve. Write or draw to explain.

6.   **Math Processes and Practices 4**   Use Diagrams David needs to divide two pieces of paper into the same number of equal shares. Look at how the first paper is divided. Show how to divide the second paper a different way.

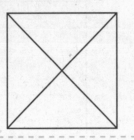

7.   **GO DEEPER**   Mrs. Lee cut two sandwiches into halves. The sandwiches are the same size. How many equal shares does she have?

_____ equal shares

8.   **THINK SMARTER**   Emma wants to cut a piece of paper into fourths. Fill in the bubbles to show all the ways she could cut the paper.

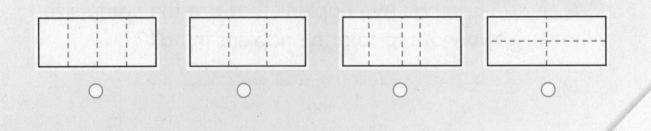

🏠 **TAKE HOME ACTIVITY** • Ask your child to draw two rectangles and show two different ways to divide them into fourths.

Problem Solving • Equal Shares

Solve. Draw to show your answer.

1. Max has square pizzas that are the same size. What are two different ways he can divide the pizzas into fourths?

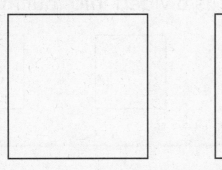

2. Lia has two pieces of paper that are the same size. What are two different ways she can divide the pieces of paper into halves?

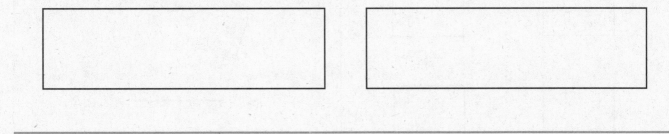

3. Frank has two crackers that are the same size. What are two different ways he can divide the cracker into fourths?

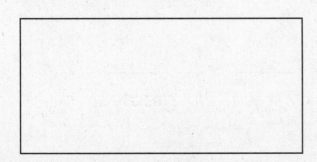 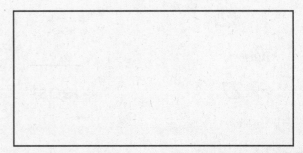

Lesson Check

1. Bree cut a piece of cardboard into fourths like this.

Circle the other shape that is divided into fourths.

Spiral Review

2. Circle the shapes with two equal parts.

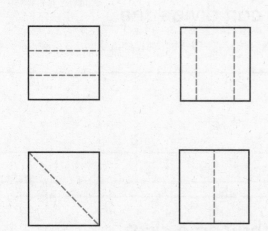

3. Circle the angles in the shape. Write how many.

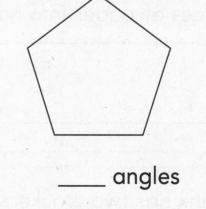

_____ angles

4. Write the numbers in order.

32

40

27

_____ _____ _____

least   greatest

Name _____

Algebra • Identify and Describe Repeating Patterns

Essential Question How can you use models to identify and describe repeating patterns?

Learning Objective You will identify and describe repeating patterns.

Listen and Draw Real World

Use cubes to copy the pattern. Draw and color the cube that comes next.

Math Talk
How did you decide which cube comes next? **Explain.**

🍎 **FOR THE TEACHER •** Read the problem. Jane uses cubes to make patterns. She asks, "What comes next in each of my patterns?"

A **repeating pattern** repeats the same things over and over again.

This **pattern core** is red square, red circle, red circle. It helps you predict what comes next.

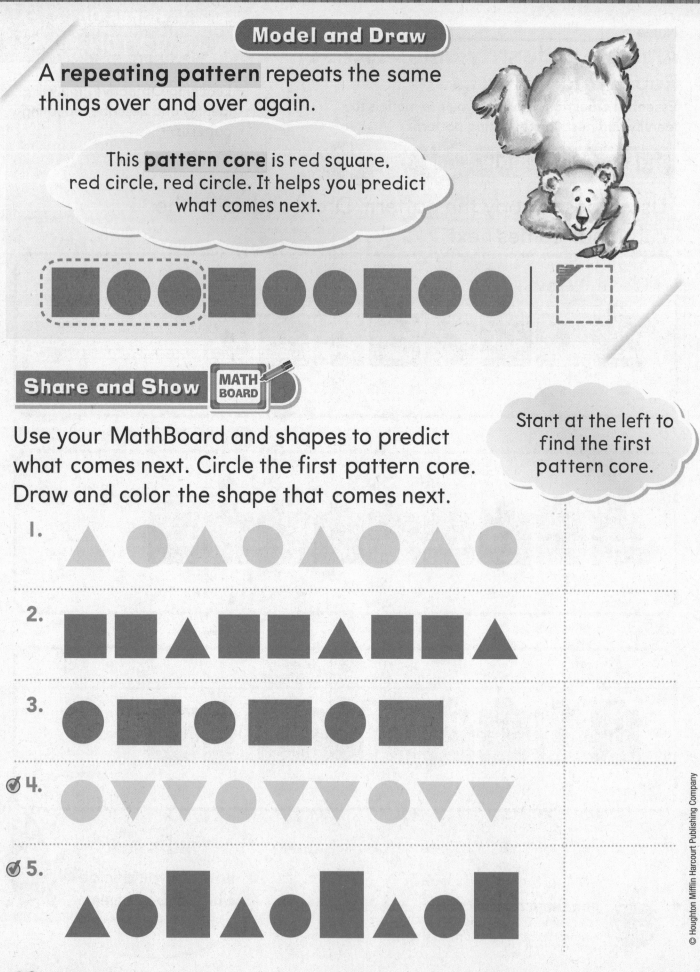

Share and Show MATH BOARD

Use your MathBoard and shapes to predict what comes next. Circle the first pattern core. Draw and color the shape that comes next.

Start at the left to find the first pattern core.

1.

2.

3.

4.

5.

Name _____

Circle the first pattern core. Draw
and color the shape that comes next.

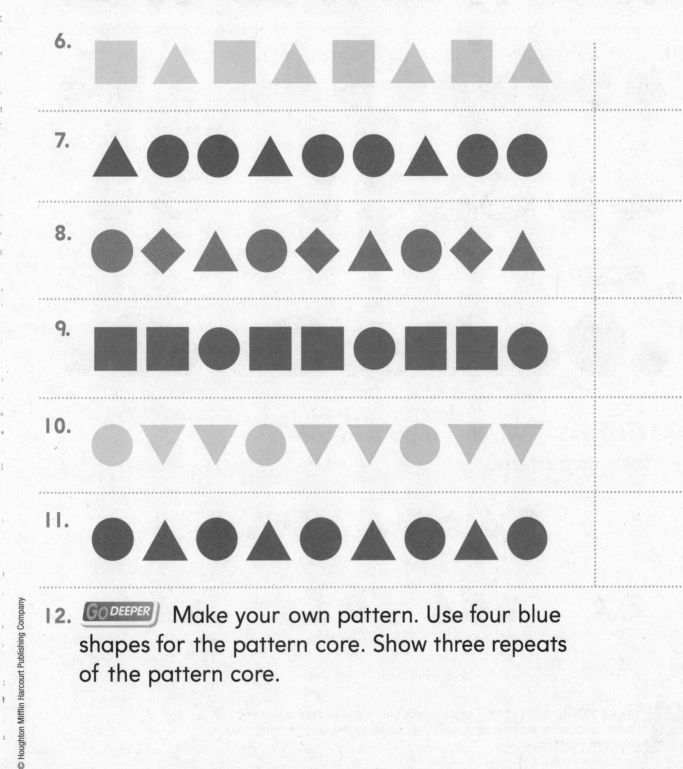

6.

7.

8.

9.

10.

11.

12. **GO DEEPER** Make your own pattern. Use four blue
shapes for the pattern core. Show three repeats
of the pattern core.

Problem Solving • Applications Real World WRITE Math

Circle the picture that comes next.

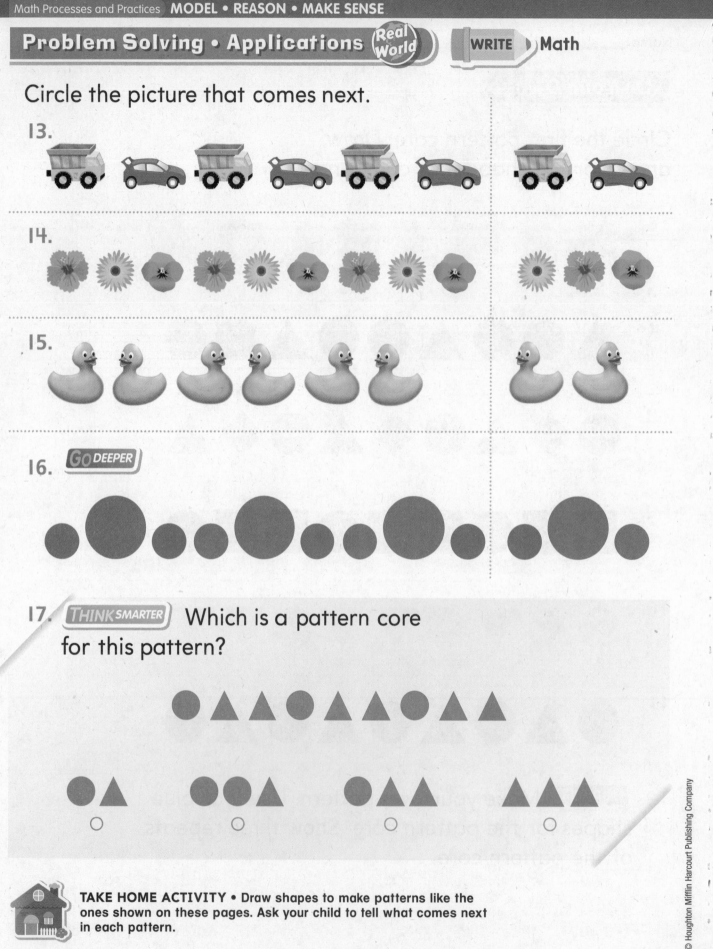

13.

14.

15.

16. GO DEEPER

17. THINK SMARTER Which is a pattern core for this pattern?

TAKE HOME ACTIVITY • Draw shapes to make patterns like the ones shown on these pages. Ask your child to tell what comes next in each pattern.

Algebra • Identify and Describe Repeating Patterns

Learning Objective You will identify and describe repeating patterns.

Circle the first pattern core.
Draw and color the shape that comes next.

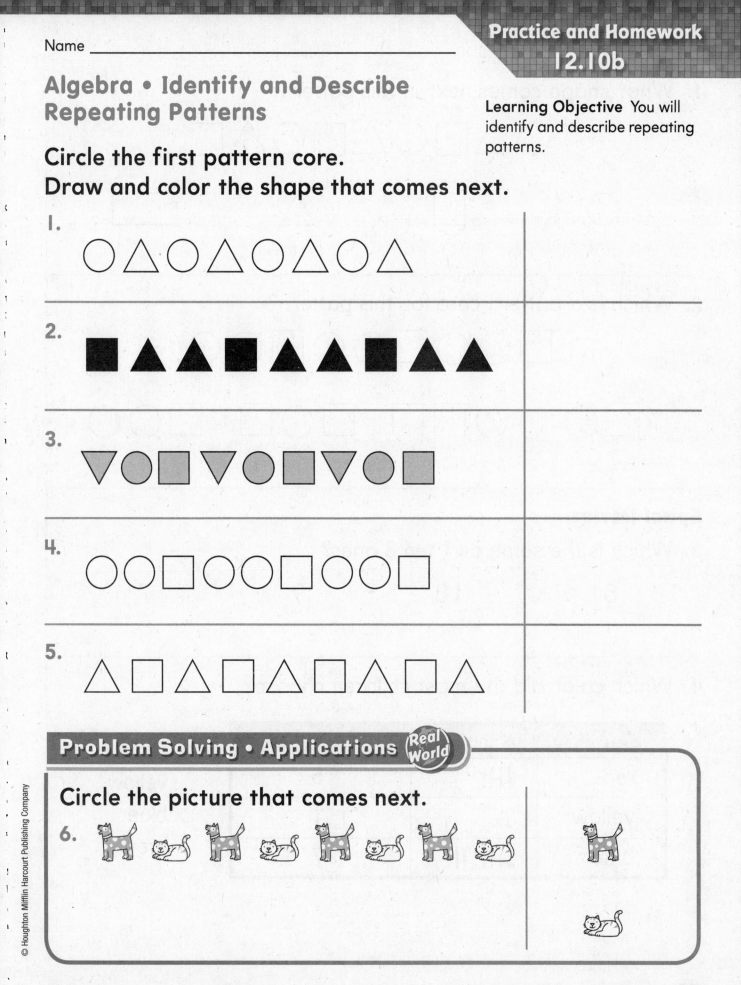

1.

2.

3.

4.

5.

Problem Solving • Applications

Circle the picture that comes next.

6.

Lesson Check

1. What shape comes next in this pattern?

○△□○△□○△□

○   □   △   ▭
○   ○   ○   ○

2. Which is a pattern core for this pattern?

□○○□○○□○○

□○   ○□□   □□○□   □○○
○   ○   ○   ○

Spiral Review

3. Which is the same as 1 ten 8 ones?

81   18   9   7
○   ○   ○   ○

4. Which color did the most children choose?

Our Favorite Color		Total
red	⊬⊬	5
yellow	I	1
blue	⊬⊬ II	7

○ red
○ yellow
○ blue
○ green

© Houghton Mifflin Harcourt Publishing Company

Name _____

Algebra: Extend Repeating Patterns

Essential Question How can you extend repeating patterns?

Learning Objective You will extend repeating patterns.

Listen and Draw *Real World*

Use ✏ and ✏. Color to show two different repeating patterns.

FOR THE TEACHER • Read the problem. Ron uses the same two colors to draw different repeating patterns. What are two patterns he can draw?

Math Talk

How are the pattern cores different in your two patterns? **Explain.**

Virginia SOL Success • 12.10c

ninety-seven **97**

Model and Draw

Find the pattern core to help you continue the pattern.

The pattern core is big rectangle, small rectangle.

The pattern core is 2 circles, 1 circle.

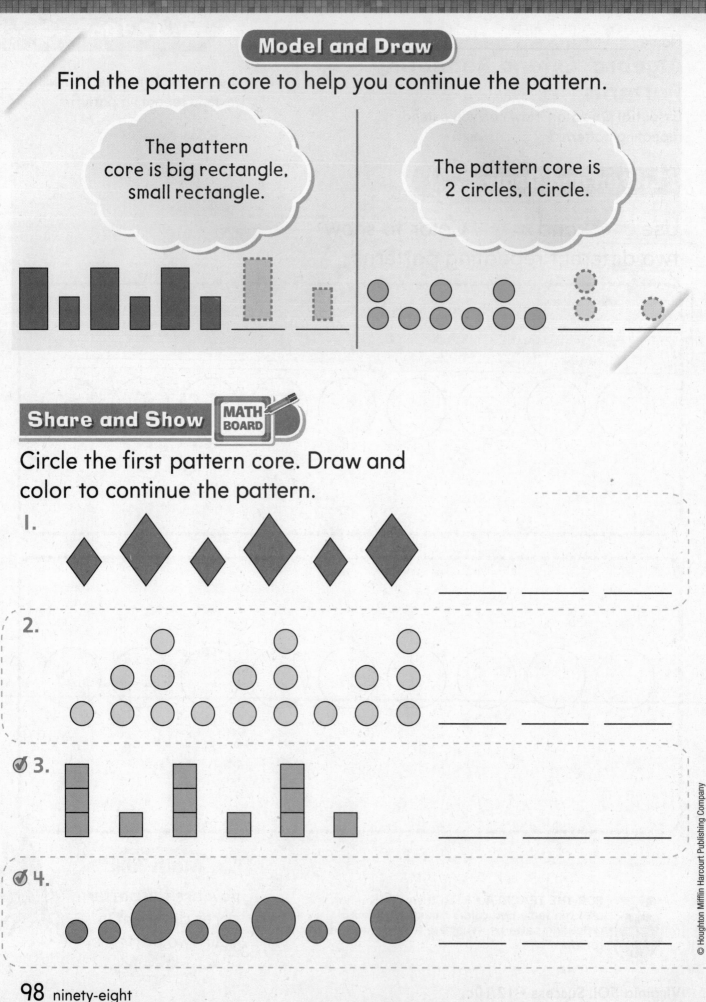

Share and Show MATH BOARD

Circle the first pattern core. Draw and color to continue the pattern.

1.

2.

3.

4.

© Houghton Mifflin Harcourt Publishing Company

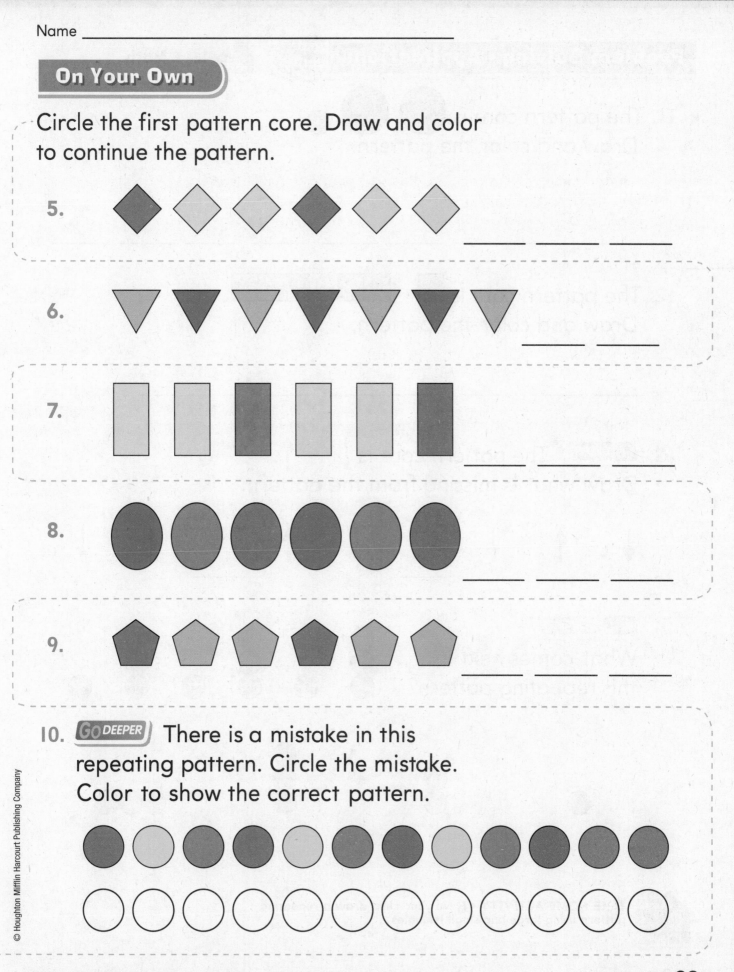

Name _____

On Your Own

Circle the first pattern core. Draw and color to continue the pattern.

5.

6.

7.

8.

9.

10. **Go DEEPER** There is a mistake in this repeating pattern. Circle the mistake. Color to show the correct pattern.

Problem Solving • Applications (Real World)   WRITE ▶ Math

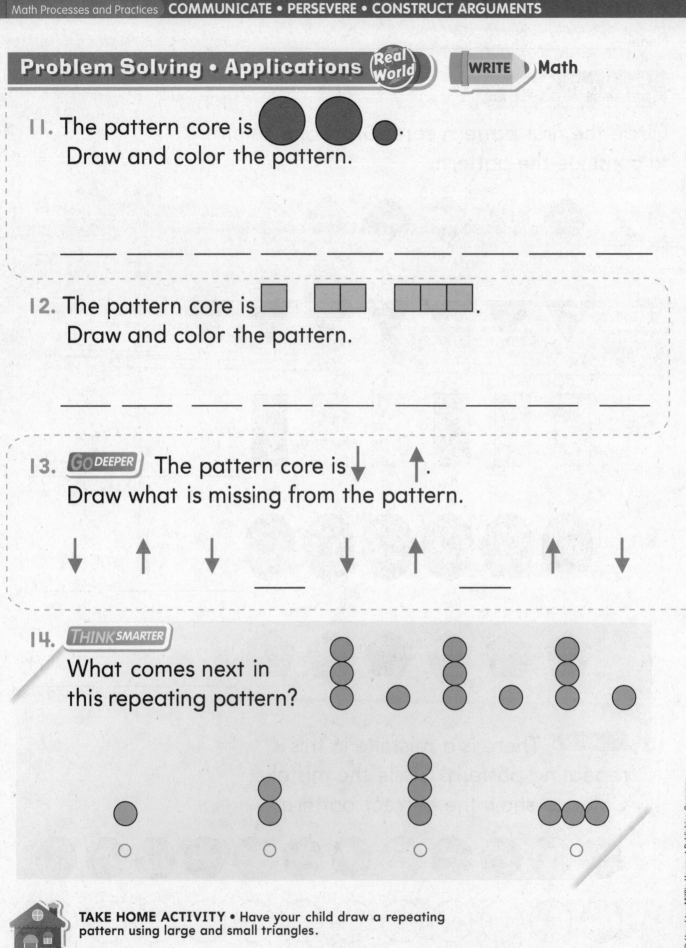

11. The pattern core is ● ● ●.
Draw and color the pattern.

_____

12. The pattern core is ⬜ ⬜⬜ ⬜⬜⬜.
Draw and color the pattern.

_____

13. GO DEEPER The pattern core is ↓ ↑.
Draw what is missing from the pattern.

↓   ↑   ↓   ↓   ↑   ↑   ↓

14. THINK SMARTER
What comes next in
this repeating pattern?

TAKE HOME ACTIVITY • Have your child draw a repeating
pattern using large and small triangles.

Name _____

Algebra • Extend Repeating Patterns

Learning Objective You will extend repeating patterns.

Circle the first pattern core.
Draw and color to continue the pattern.

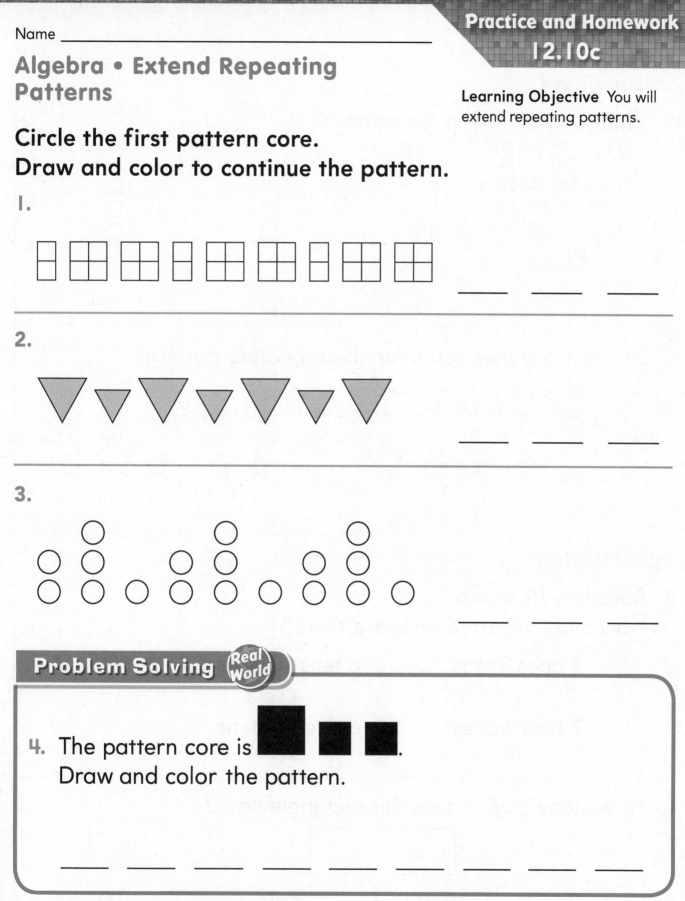

1.

_____ _____ _____ _____

2.

_____ _____ _____ _____

3.

_____ _____ _____ _____

Problem Solving Real World

4. The pattern core is ■ ■ ■.
Draw and color the pattern.

_____ _____ _____ _____ _____ _____ _____ _____

Virginia SOL Success • 12.10c

Lesson Check

1. What comes next in the pattern?

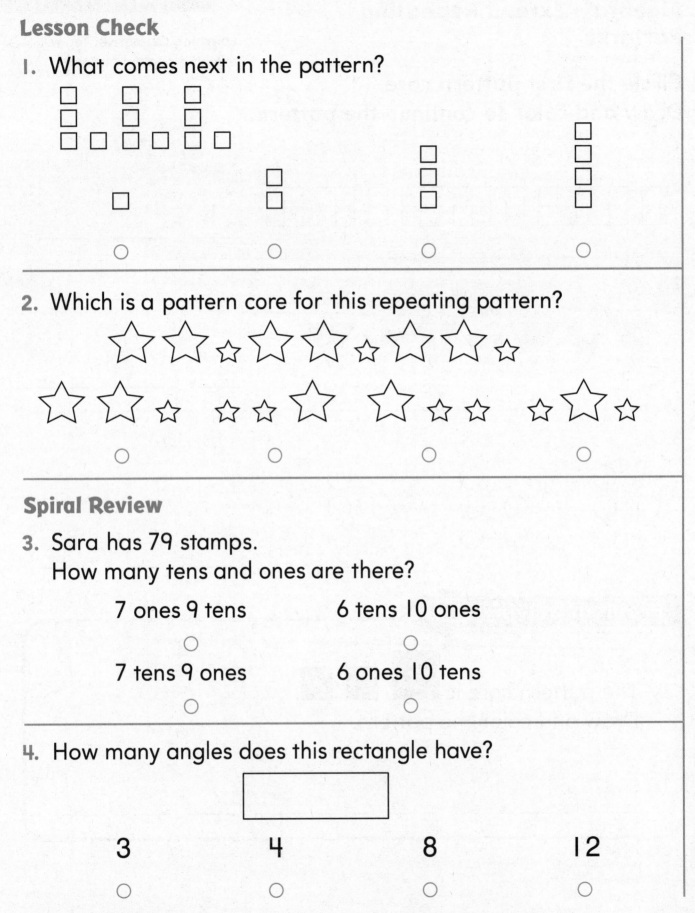

2. Which is a pattern core for this repeating pattern?

Spiral Review

3. Sara has 79 stamps.
   How many tens and ones are there?

   7 ones 9 tens   6 tens 10 ones
        ○   ○
   7 tens 9 ones   6 ones 10 tens
        ○   ○

4. How many angles does this rectangle have?

   3   4   8   12
   ○   ○   ○   ○

Algebra • Create and Transfer Repeating Patterns

Essential Question How can you create a repeating pattern and then show it a different way?

Learning Objective You will learn to create and show repeating patterns in different ways.

Listen and Draw (Real World)   (Hands On)

Use pattern blocks to copy the pattern core.
Then repeat the pattern. Draw the blocks you use.

_____ _____ _____

Use letters to copy the pattern core. Then repeat the pattern.

A   A   B   _____ _____ _____ _____

Use numbers to copy the pattern core. Then repeat the pattern.

1   1   2   _____ _____ _____ _____ _____

Math Talk   Math Processes and Practices ①

Looks at the patterns above. How are the patterns alike? How are they different? **Explain.**

FOR THE TEACHER • Read the problem. Sam used these pattern blocks to make a pattern core. How can Sam use blocks to repeat the pattern? Have students draw to show their work. Then have them repeat the letter and number patterns.

Use these shapes to make a pattern.

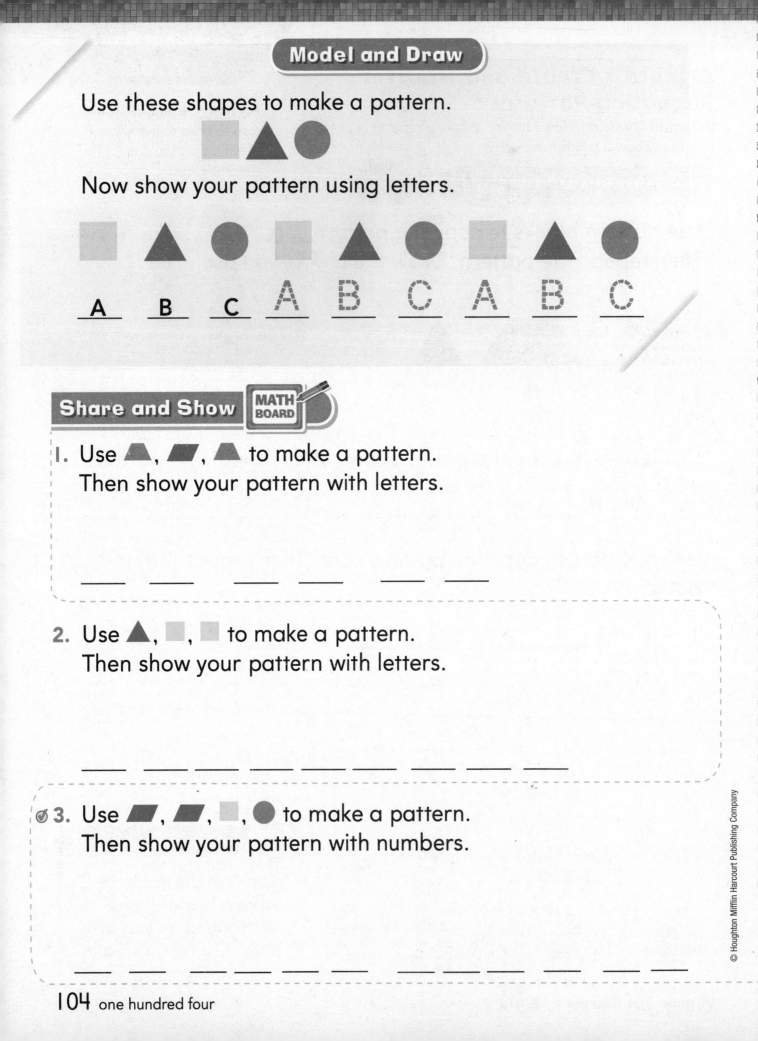

Now show your pattern using letters.

A   B   C   A   B   C   A   B   C

Share and Show [MATH BOARD]

1. Use ▲, ▰, ▲ to make a pattern.
Then show your pattern with letters.

___ ___ ___ ___ ___

2. Use ▲, ▪, ▪ to make a pattern.
Then show your pattern with letters.

___ ___ ___ ___ ___ ___

3. Use ▰, ▰, ▪, ● to make a pattern.
Then show your pattern with numbers.

___ ___ ___ ___ ___

On Your Own

4. Use 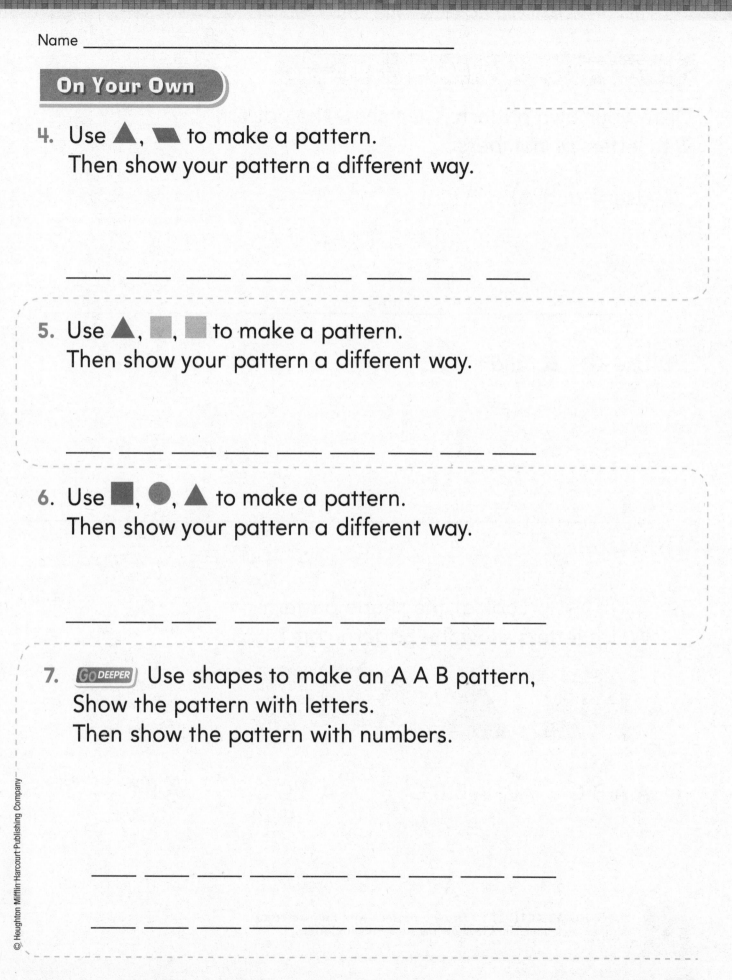 △, ▰ to make a pattern.
   Then show your pattern a different way.

   ___ ___ ___ ___ ___ ___ ___ ___ ___

5. Use △, ■, ■ to make a pattern.
   Then show your pattern a different way.

   ___ ___ ___ ___ ___ ___ ___ ___ ___ ___

6. Use ■, ●, △ to make a pattern.
   Then show your pattern a different way.

   ___ ___ ___ ___ ___ ___ ___ ___ ___

7. **GO DEEPER** Use shapes to make an A A B pattern,
   Show the pattern with letters.
   Then show the pattern with numbers.

   ___ ___ ___ ___ ___ ___ ___ ___ ___

   ___ ___ ___ ___ ___ ___ ___ ___ ___

Problem Solving • Applications Real World

Draw your own pattern. Then show the pattern
with letters or numbers.

8. Use ● and ▲.

_____

9. Use ◤, ▲, and ●.

_____

10. **THINK SMARTER** Look at the shape pattern.
Which letters show the pattern core?

A A B C   A B B C   A B C C   A B C
○   ○   ○   ○

TAKE HOME ACTIVITY • Draw a pattern with four different
shapes. Ask your child to show the pattern with letters.

Algebra • Create and Transfer Repeating Patterns

Learning Objective You will learn to create and show repeating patterns in different ways.

1. Use ○, □, □ to make a pattern.
   Then show the pattern a different way.

   ___ ___ ___ ___ ___ ___ ___ ___ ___ ___ ___ ___

2. Use □, ○ to make a pattern.
   Then show the pattern a different way.

   ___ ___ ___ ___ ___ ___ ___ ___ ___ ___ ___ ___

3. Use ○, □, □ to make a pattern.
   Then show the pattern a different way.

   ___ ___ ___ ___ ___ ___ ___ ___ ___ ___ ___ ___

Problem Solving Real World

Draw shapes to show the same pattern a different way.

4. 1   1   2   1   1   2

   _____

WRITE Math Look at the number pattern in Exercise 4. How did you know how many different kinds of shapes to draw?

Lesson Check

1. Use ▢, ○, △, to make a pattern.
   Then show the pattern
   a different way.

   ___ ___ ___ ___ ___ ___ ___

Spiral Review

2. What is the difference?

$$12 - 9 = \underline{\qquad}$$

    2   3   4   5

    ○   ○   ○   ○

---

3. Which shape has 3 angles?

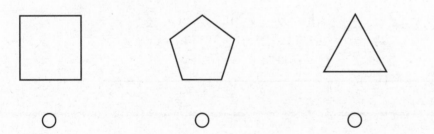

    ○   ○   ○   ○

Algebra • Identify and Describe Growing Patterns

Essential Question How can you use models to identify and describe growing patterns?

Learning Objective You will learn to identify and describe growing patterns.

Listen and Draw

Use and  to copy the patterns. Write how many.

_____   _____   _____

_____   _____   _____

FOR THE TEACHER • Read the following. Jenny arranged cubes to make two patterns. What patterns did Jenny make?

Math Talk
Describe how these patterns grow.

Model and Draw

Each part of a pattern can grow to make a growing pattern. What will come next?

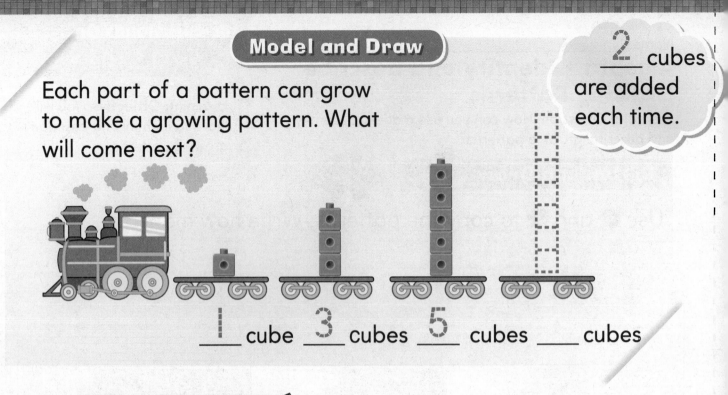

____ cubes are added each time.

____ cube   3 cubes   5 cubes   ____ cubes

Share and Show   MATH BOARD

Copy the growing pattern. Use your MathBoard, , and ▪. Write how many. Then predict what will come next. Circle your answer.

1.

_____   _____   _____

✓ 2.

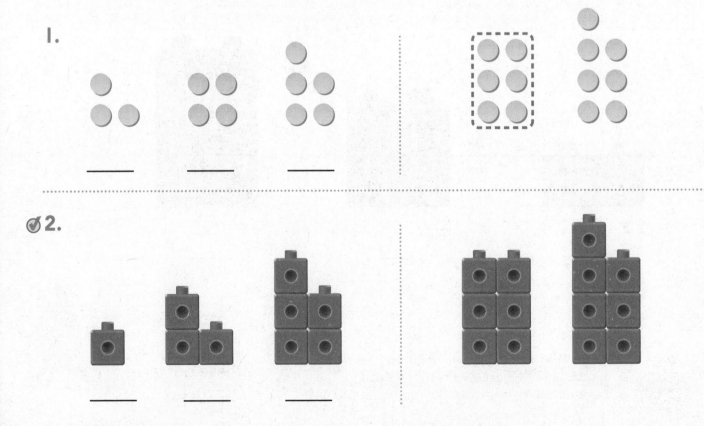

_____   _____   _____

110   one hundred ten

Name _____

On Your Own

Copy the growing pattern. Use your MathBoard, ⬤, and ▦. Write how many. Then predict what will come next. Circle your answer.

3.

_____   _____   _____

4.

_____   _____   _____

5.

_____   _____   _____

6. **GO DEEPER** Circle to show what will come next.

Problem Solving • Applications (Real World) WRITE Math

What will come next? Circle your answer.

7.

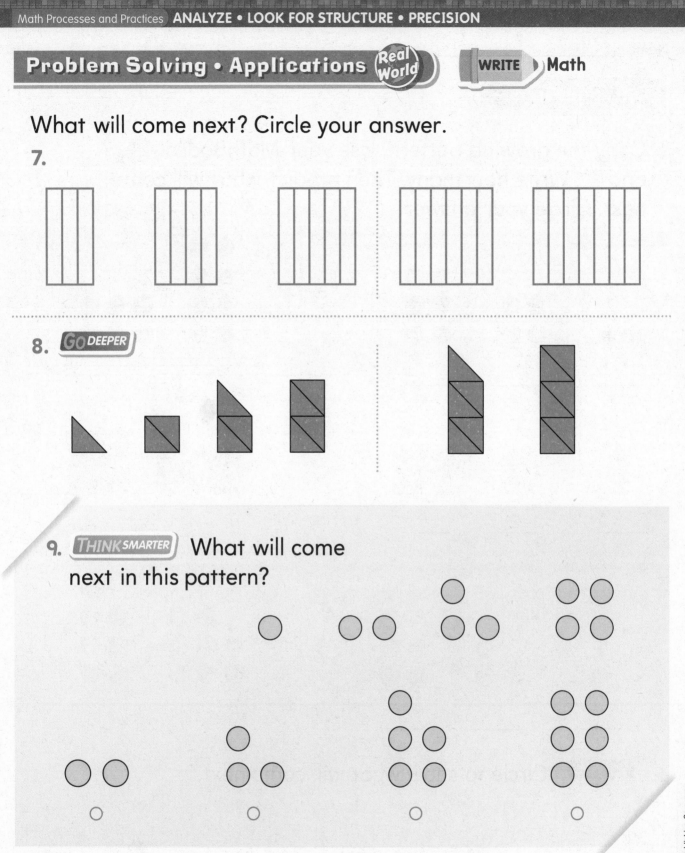

8. GO DEEPER

9. THINK SMARTER What will come next in this pattern?

Algebra • Identify and Describe Growing Patterns

Look at the growing pattern. Write how many. Then predict what will come next. Circle your answer.

Learning Objective You will learn to identify and describe growing patterns.

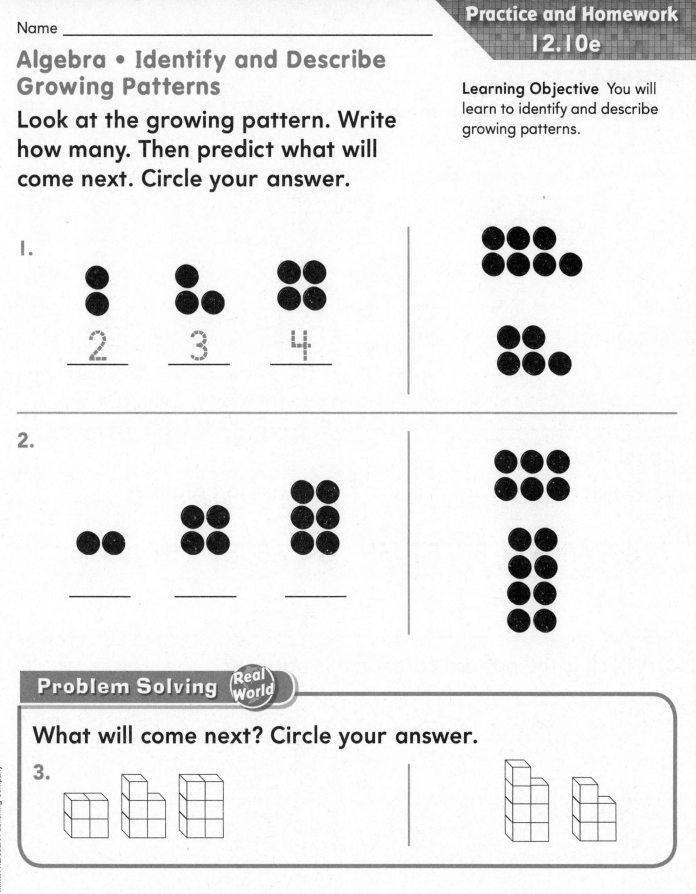

1.

2 _____ 3 _____ 4 _____

2.

_____ _____ _____

Problem Solving (Real World)

What will come next? Circle your answer.

3.

Lesson Check

1. What comes next in the pattern?

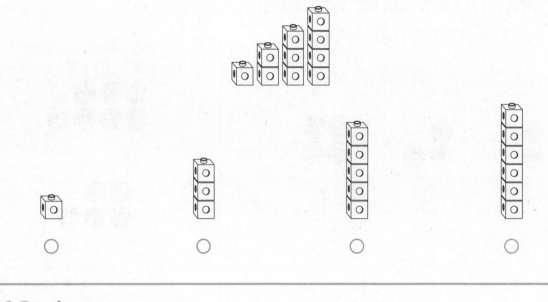

○   ○   ○   ○

Spiral Review

2. Which numbers are in order from least to greatest?

87, 65, 51   87, 51, 65   51, 65, 87   51, 87, 65

○   ○   ○   ○

---

3. Which is the pattern core for this pattern?

○ ◯ ○ ◯ ○ ◯ ○ ◯

◯ ◯   ○ ○   ○ ◯   ◯

○   ○   ○   ○

Name _____

Algebra • Extend Growing Patterns

Essential Question How can you extend a growing pattern?

Learning Objective You will learn to extend growing patterns.

Listen and Draw (Real World)

Use ⬤ to copy the pattern. Write how many.

_____ _____ _____ _____ _____

_____ _____ _____ _____

FOR THE TEACHER • Read the following. Luis saw these patterns in a puzzle book. How can he show the patterns with numbers?

Math Talk

Describe the patterns.

What will come next?
How will it grow?

Draw to continue the
growing pattern.

<u> 1 </u> cube is added each time.

<u> 5 </u> cubes come next.

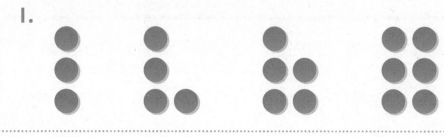

Predict what will come next.
Draw to continue the growing pattern.

1.

_____

☑ 2.

_____

☑ 3.

_____

Name _____

On Your Own

Predict what will come next.
Draw to continue the growing pattern.

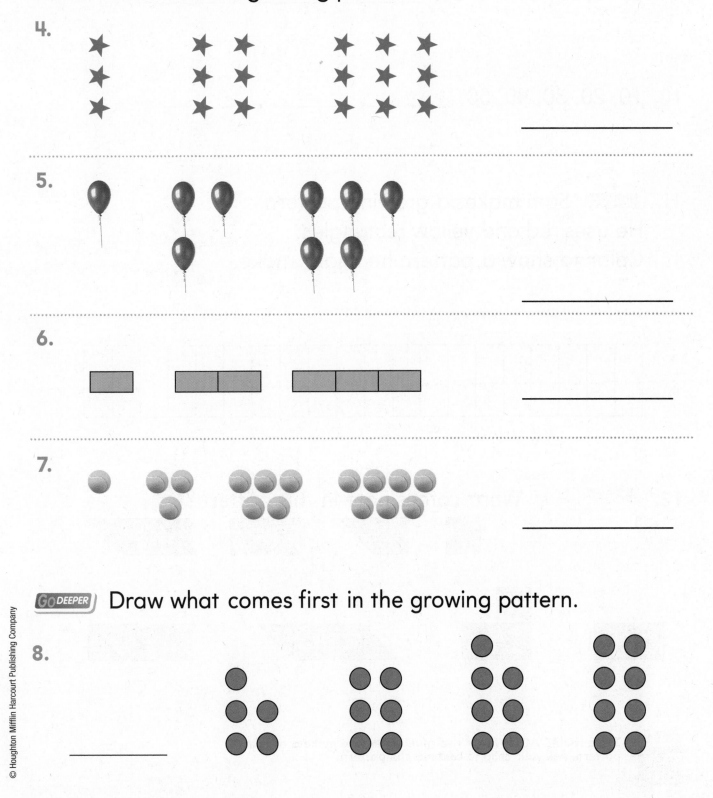

4.

_____

5.

_____

6.

_____

7.

_____

Go DEEPER Draw what comes first in the growing pattern.

8.

_____

Problem Solving • Applications (Real World)   WRITE ▸ Math

Use numbers to continue the growing pattern.

9. 5, 10, 15, 20, 25, 30, _____, _____, _____

10. 10, 20, 30, 40, 50, _____, _____, _____

11. GO DEEPER Sam makes a growing pattern.
He uses red and yellow rectangles.
Color to show a pattern he might make.

12. THINK SMARTER What comes next in this pattern?

TAKE HOME ACTIVITY • Use small objects to make a growing pattern. Ask your child to continue the pattern.

Algebra • Extend Growing Patterns

Learning Objective You will learn to extend growing patterns.

Predict what will come next in the growing pattern. Draw to continue the pattern.

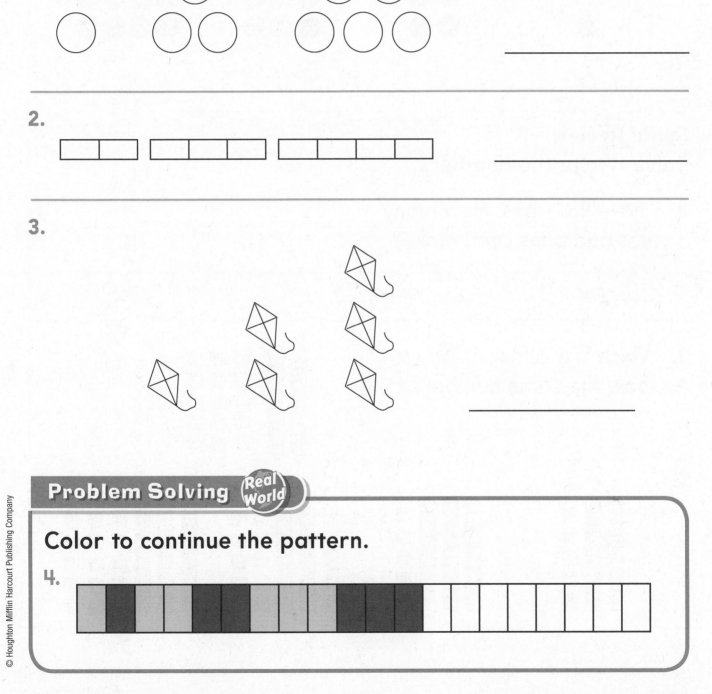

1.

_____

2.

_____

3.

_____

Problem Solving Real World

Color to continue the pattern.

4.

Lesson Check

1. What comes next in the growing pattern?

○   ○   ○   ○

Spiral Review

Solve. Write the numbers.

2. I have 43 cubes. How many tens and ones can I make?

_____ tens   _____ ones

3. Which is a different way to show the same number?

○   ○   ○   ○

Name _____

Algebra • Create Growing Patterns

Essential Question How can you create a growing pattern?

Learning Objective You will create a growing pattern.

Listen and Draw (Real World)

Use ⬤ to copy the pattern.
Draw and write to show what comes next.

1   3   5   7   _____   _____

🍎 **FOR THE TEACHER** • Read the problem. Ann is creating a growing pattern. How many counters will she use for the next two steps of the pattern?

Math Talk

Describe the growing pattern.

You can use  to create a growing pattern.

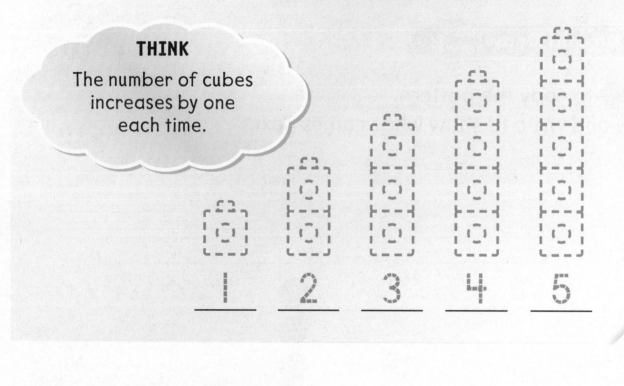

THINK
The number of cubes increases by one each time.

1   2   3   4   5

Share and Show MATH BOARD

☑ 1. Use ● to create a growing pattern.
Draw the pattern. Write the numbers.

On Your Own

2. Use ◼ to create a growing pattern.
   Draw the pattern. Write the numbers.

   ___ ___ ___ ___ ___

3. GO DEEPER Ava created a growing pattern
   that was a skip counting pattern.
   The pattern grew by 2 numbers each step.
   Write the growing pattern Ava might have created.

   _____

Problem Solving • Applications (Real World)

4. Use ☆ and △ to create a growing pattern.
   Draw your pattern.

Describe your growing pattern.

_____

_____

5. THINK SMARTER Use ▮ to create a growing pattern.
   Draw your pattern. Write the numbers.

_____   _____   _____   _____   _____

TAKE HOME ACTIVITY • Give your child a handful of pennies or some other object they can use to create a growing pattern. Have your child explain the steps they used to create the growing pattern.

Algebra • Create Growing Patterns

Learning Objective You will create a growing pattern.

1. Use ⌇ to create a growing pattern.
   Draw and describe your pattern.

. . . .

_____

_____

Problem Solving (Real World)

2. Mackenzie uses the numbers 1 to 10 to create a growing pattern. Write or draw the pattern.

____, ____, ____, ____, ____, ____, ____, ____, ____, ____

Show Mackenzie's pattern a different way.

_____

Lesson Check

1. Use ◖▬▬▬▷ to create a growing pattern.
   Draw your pattern.

Spiral Review

2. What will come next in this growing pattern?
   Draw and write to show.

_____   _____   _____   _____